Blaenavon Ironworks
and World Heritage Landscape

Peter Wakelin BA, MSocSc, PhD, FSA

C000195920

The Industrial Revolution in Iron and Coal

Cyfarthfa, Dowlais, Tredegar and Blaenavon were once names that echoed around the world. These were among the Welsh ironworks that led the organizational and technological development of the iron industry during the Industrial Revolution, and helped to transform society. At the end of the eighteenth and the beginning of the nineteenth centuries a string of new ironworks was developed along the northern rim of the south Wales coalfield, making it the greatest iron-producing district in the world. Blaenavon's highly advanced iron-making operation, embarked on in 1787, is part of this story. Its extensive historic landscape, now a World Heritage Site, remains a microcosm of the formative years of the Industrial Revolution.

By 1830 south Wales made forty per cent of all the iron in Britain — itself the largest iron-producing country in the world. Cheap, plentiful iron was vital to the development of engines, tools and machines which transformed productivity. Iron rails and ships carried people and materials around the world; and iron enabled new kinds of buildings and engineering structures, from the Iron Bridge at Coalbrookdale in Shropshire to the Crystal Palace.

If iron was the key material of the industrial age, the coal produced at places like Blaenavon was its fuel. It was used to smelt the iron itself, fuelled steam engines, supported myriad industrial processes and warmed the homes of the new labour force. By the end of the nineteenth century more coal was exported from south Wales than from any coalfield in the world.

Furnaces to smelt iron had been built in south Wales from the sixteenth century onwards and made use of local supplies of iron ore. But these early ironworks were limited in output: they were single-furnace operations, water powered and fuelled by charcoal. The new ironworks that burst into south Wales between the 1750s and the 1830s were wholly different. Vast territories rich in coal, iron ore and limestone were leased, and the latest methods of production were applied on a grand, coordinated scale. The new generation of works all had several furnaces — now fired by coal in the form of coke — and they operated as a series of integrated processes, from the mining of the raw materials through to the manufacturing of wrought iron. Many were also steam powered. By the 1790s Cyfarthfa Ironworks at Merthyr Tydfil was the largest in the world, with 2,000 workers, to be superseded only by neighbouring Dowlais, just thirty years later, with a workforce of 6,000.

The sudden exploitation of the coalfield's mineral wealth turned the region upside down. The population grew faster than almost any other part of Britain, with immigration first from rural Wales and then from further afield. Until the mid-eighteenth century, the upland strip where the ironworks were concentrated had a negligible population, but by the 1840s it had drawn in 150,000 people. As a result, by 1851 Welsh people employed in industry exceeded those in agriculture, giving Wales a claim to be the very first industrial nation.

The Blaenavon landscape still contains evidence of all the characteristics that defined the Industrial Revolution. The ironworks demonstrates the centralization of production, the use of mechanization and the rapid technological change that brought about the astonishing hundredfold increase in iron output from south Wales between the 1780s and the 1860s. The canals, horse tramroads and locomotive railways — which connected producers to the markets of the world — can all be traced. Population growth and urbanization are evident in the housing thrown up on these previously barren hillsides as Blaenavon grew from a few dozen inhabitants to 13,000 at its peak in 1921. The character of industrial society can be understood from the contrast between the ironmasters' dwellings and the cottages of the new working classes, and from the schools and social institutions that developed, the Nonconformist chapels, and the shops and public houses which provided the consumer goods that industrial wages could buy.

Opposite: Coalbrookdale by Night, *painted in 1801 by Philip James de Loutherbourg (1740–1812), is one of the defining images of the early Industrial Revolution. Artists and new migrants to industrial areas alike were astonished by the transformation taking place before their eyes in society and the natural world. For many it must have seemed as if the earth was being turned literally inside out: minerals were hauled from underground and made molten in infernal heat. The painting shows the Bedlam Furnaces in what was to become known as the Ironbridge Gorge. The furnaces and their engine house are on the far right, but the whole sky has been turned red by the coke heaps behind them (Detail — Science Museum/ Science & Society Picture Library).*

A token from the Blaenavon truck shop (National Museum of Wales).

A History of Blaenavon Ironworks and Landscape

Lord Abergavenny's Hills

South Wales saw a frantic land rush in the late eighteenth century as investors sought virgin territories for new ironworks. A few entrepreneurs had already demonstrated the enormous potential of the northern rim of the coalfield, by establishing works such as Hirwaun (1757), Dowlais (1759) and Sirhowy (1778). The partners who planned Blaenavon Ironworks arrived in 1787, when the opportunity arose to lease 12,000 acres (4,855ha) of upland at the head of the Afon Lwyd from the marquess of Abergavenny: a territory fit to support a substantial new operation. It was among the last really large landholdings still to be had on the coalfield rim. By October one of their competitors was writing, 'all hope of Lord Abergavenny's Royalty is at an end'.

The partners were Midlands businessmen. Their leader was Thomas Hill (1736–1824) of Amblecote in Staffordshire, a banker with industrial interests. He was joined by his sister's husband, Thomas Hopkins (d.1793), a Staffordshire ironmaster, and by Benjamin Pratt of Oldswinford (1742–94), whose family had been partners in earlier Welsh ironworks. Like many investors experienced in the competition for resources and complexities of land ownership in intensively developed iron-making districts, the three men saw the value of bringing the latest innovations to a fresh location.

The iron industry had evolved steadily up to this point. Temporary 'bloomeries' had been used to make small quantities of iron since the Iron Age. Blast furnaces had been introduced to Britain in the fifteenth century, in the form of stone towers containing a furnace blown by waterwheel-powered bellows. These produced molten iron that was run into sand beds in the floor of a cast house to solidify as cast-iron objects or as 'pigs' of raw metal.

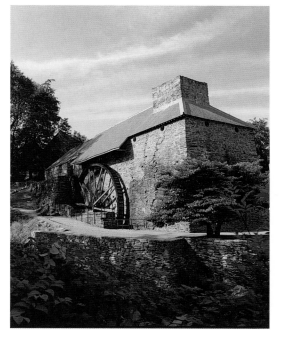

Cast iron contained around three to four per cent carbon, and only once this had been reduced, by converting it in a forge to wrought ('worked') iron, could it be rolled or drawn in mills, or used by smiths to make innumerable other goods.

Although blast furnaces allowed the continuous production of cast iron, they were still limited in productivity. One of the main factors was the use of charcoal as a fuel. Charcoal making was slow and labour-intensive, and required timber to be grown locally, as it fragmented during transportation. Only isolated, single furnaces could therefore be supported. Moreover, since charcoal was easily crushed, furnaces were limited in height, and hence capacity. The technique of using mineral coal instead of charcoal, by part-burning it to make coke, was pioneered by Abraham Darby I (1678–1717) at Coalbrookdale

Left: Dyfi Furnace, an excellently preserved example of the isolated charcoal-fuelled iron furnaces which smelted iron before the growth of the highly organized coke iron industry of the Industrial Revolution. The waterwheel that powered the bellows is on the left.

Above: A portrait of Thomas Hill I, the leading partner in the ironworks from the start. Hill was a Midlands banker with industrial interests. His descendants owned the works until it was made a joint stock company in 1836 (Godfrey Hill).

Opposite: The Industrial Revolution comes to Blaenavon. The new ironworks in a detail from Sir Richard Colt Hoare's watercolour (see pp. 20–21) showing the blowing-engine house amid the furnaces. The bell in the gable of the cast house hints at the new industrial discipline of shift-work (© Yale Centre for British Art, Paul Mellon Collection, USA/ Bridgeman Art Library).

The remaining bank of furnaces at Cyfarthfa Ironworks in Merthyr Tydfil, the largest ironworks in the world from the 1790s to the 1830s. With its four great iron companies, Merthyr Tydfil became the world's leading iron-making centre and the largest town in Wales.

Below: The lease of 'Lord Abergavenny's Hills' to the three Blaenavon partners, signed finally in November 1789, by which time they had virtually completed building the works (Gwent Record Office).

in Shropshire in 1709. He concentrated on making cast objects, but by the 1750s his son, Abraham Darby II (1711–1763), had improved the process to make pigs suitable for converting to wrought iron. Since coke could be produced in large quantities wherever there was suitable coal, ironworks could now be built with several furnaces on the same site. Water supplies were not always sufficient for several furnaces (or for year-round operation). But with the introduction of steam engines to recirculate water in the 1740s, and after 1776 to blow furnaces directly, the industry was no longer at the mercy of wood and water.

The Blaenavon partners would have seen the area as a perfect location for a large iron-working enterprise where all the newly developed technology could be combined. (Their landholding was so large that they were able to sub-let sites for two further works.) Seams of coal and iron ore lay near the surface, and limestone — needed as a flux to help remove impurities during smelting — outcropped just beyond. In addition, clay fit for making firebricks to line the furnaces was available, and there was sandstone for building. Although iron ore had probably been exploited on the local hills for two thousand years — and was still being dug for the Hanbury family's charcoal-fired furnace in Pontypool — the valley and the moors behind were still sparsely populated. Everything was about to change forever.

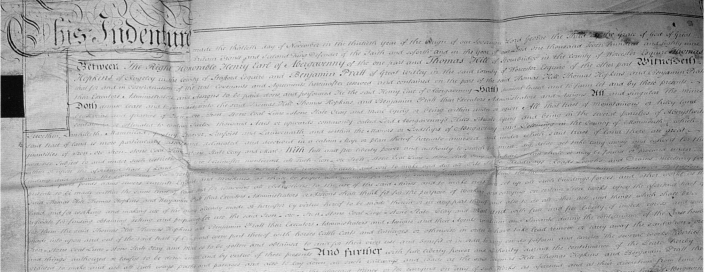

Thomas Hornor's remarkable watercolour of about 1817 showing rolling mills at Merthyr Tydfil. The puddling furnaces are throwing light up into the sky from the building with the tall chimneys. Rolling mills in the building to the right are powered by a steam engine (National Museum of Wales).

Establishing the Ironworks 1787–99

The lease of Blaenavon was signed finally in November 1789, by which time the partners had nearly completed the ironworks and the infrastructure to support it. They had chosen an elevated site, well located for minerals yet unpromising for water power. Blaenavon was to be only the second works in the world designed for steam power, after John Wilkinson's Snedshill works in Shropshire (p. 37). The partners planned several furnaces and had built Furnaces 1, 2 and 3 by 1792: Blaenavon may have been the first ironworks anywhere to be devised as a multi-furnace site from the outset. It was straight away one of the handful of most productive ironworks in the world and it made a significant contribution to the trebling of iron output from south Wales that took place during its first eight years in operation.

Only one aspect of the operation was not at the cutting edge of the industry: it did not have a puddling works to make wrought iron. Patented in 1784 by Henry Cort (1741–1800), the puddling process enabled large forges to be built alongside smelting works by allowing coal rather than charcoal to be used efficiently in converting pig iron into wrought iron. Richard Crawshay (1739–1810) at Cyfarthfa

Ironworks was the first to make use of puddling, building such extensive forges and rolling mills to exploit the process from 1787 onwards that it became known as 'the Welsh method'. Although there were some small refineries at Blaenavon, the partners initially sold raw pig iron for others to manufacture.

The first depiction of the ironworks was a watercolour by Sir Richard Colt Hoare (1758–1838) painted within a few years of its construction (pp. 4, 20). This gives a vivid impression of how the hillside had been cut away to create a vertical face against which the tall furnaces were built, with an engine house between them. The works itself stood on the very edge of the coal measures, but behind it the partners opened mines and quarries, built brickworks and laid out primitive railways to deliver iron ore, coal and limestone to the tops of the furnaces, ready for smelting.

The primitive railways or 'tramroads' carried wagons that were drawn by horses or moved by gravity on gently graded routes. Such lines were used throughout the iron-making districts of south Wales, which probably had more miles of primitive railways than anywhere else in the world. The earliest types of tramroad at Blaenavon were 'railroads', with iron edge rails (see diagram). From the late 1790s, however, until the arrival of locomotive railways in the area in the 1850s, 'plateways' were the preferred form of tramroad, on which light flangeless wheels ran on L-shaped plates.

Below: The earliest horse-drawn tramroads at Blaenavon were edge railways (below) built from 1788 onwards, which may possibly have used the first ever all-iron rails. From the early nineteenth century, L-shaped plateways (bottom) were introduced. Stone sleeper blocks remaining from the tramroads can be found throughout the landscape. There were 1,500 tramroad wagons in the Christmas stock accounts for 1850, when standard-gauge locomotive railways were being introduced (Illustration by Michael Blackmore).

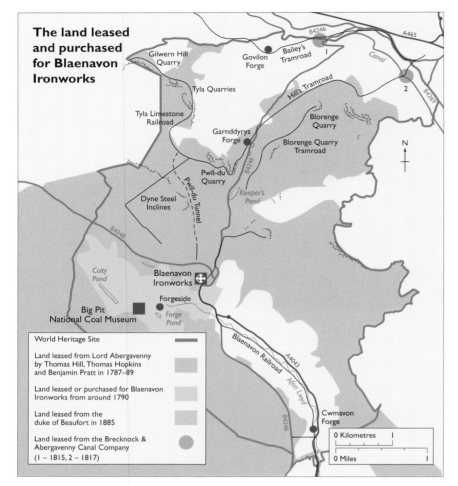

The land leased and purchased for Blaenavon Ironworks

Gilwern Hill Quarry
Govilon Forge
Bailey's Tramroad
Canal
A465
B4269
Tyla Quarries
Hill's Tramroad
1
2
Tyla Limestone Railroad
Blorenge Quarry
Garnddyrys Forge
Blorenge Quarry Tramroad
N
Pwll-du Quarry
Keeper's Pond
Dyne Steel Inclines
Pwll-du Tunnel
B4246
B4248
Coity Pond
Blaenavon Ironworks
Big Pit National Coal Museum
Forgeside
Forge Pond
Blaenavon Railroad
A4043
Afon Lwyd
B4246
Cwmavon Forge

World Heritage Site
Land leased from Lord Abergavenny by Thomas Hill, Thomas Hopkins and Benjamin Pratt in 1787–89
Land leased or purchased for Blaenavon Ironworks from around 1790
Land leased from the duke of Beaufort in 1885
Land leased from the Brecknock & Abergavenny Canal Company (1 – 1815, 2 – 1817)

0 Kilometres   1
0 Miles   1

A tramroad wagon from Sir Richard Colt Hoare's watercolour of Blaenavon Ironworks, about 1798 (© Yale Centre for British Art, Paul Mellon Collection, USA/ Bridgeman Art Library).

Hoare's companion on his journey, Archdeacon William Coxe (1748–1828), was taken with this new mode of transport, and wrote, 'the cars filled with coals or iron, and gliding along occasionally without horses, impress the traveller, who is unaccustomed to such spectacles, with pleasing astonishment'. A substantial investment was the construction of an eight- or ten-arched bridge to cross a nearby ravine, which Hoare drew: it is believed to be the first ever railway viaduct (p. 60).

Further transport improvements were necessary for the products of this upland area to reach their markets. Initially, finished iron was carried by packhorses, but in 1791 Thomas Hill became one of the promoters for the Monmouthshire Canal. Horses could pull far greater loads on water than on roads, and 3,000 miles (4,800km) of waterway were built or improved in Britain within a few decades in the late eighteenth century. Canals and linking tramroads were built up most of the main south Wales valleys in the 1790s. By 1796, the 11-mile (17.5km) stretch of the Monmouthshire Canal was complete from the shipping quays at Newport to Pontnewynydd, near Pontypool. A tramroad, of the railroad type, connecting Blaenavon to the projected canal terminus had been built three years earlier in 1793.

Workers were needed in large numbers for the new industrial operation. Within four years the partners had built enough terraced houses to accommodate up to 200 people. The surviving houses at the ironworks itself were probably built in 1788 to attract key personnel from Staffordshire to help set up the enterprise, along with a manager's house, offices and a shop for the new community. Other rows of houses were placed where workers were needed to dig coal or iron ore, quarry limestone or manage stockpiles of raw materials. As more people came into the area housing pressure increased, and by 1798 the workforce had grown to some 350. Even the viaduct was brought into service, its arches doubling as dwellings (p. 60). Coxe wrote, 'At some distance, the works have the appearance of a small town, surrounded with heaps of ore, coal, and limestone, and enlivened with all the bustle of activity of an opulent and increasing establishment.'

Experienced colliers, clerks, surveyors, furnacemen and foremen were brought from the Midlands, but much of the workforce flooded in from rural Wales, and the area remained Welsh-speaking. Wages were high compared with those in agricultural areas and all of the family could find work. Women often made up one in ten of the workforce in early iron-making communities, and many children were employed. However, life in new settlements could be hard. Digging coal and iron ore, quarrying limestone, making coke and preparing the pig beds were gruelling — most people worked twelve-hour shifts, and the furnaces operated day and night. Sometimes food was in short supply and, in the 1790s, grain riots were endemic in south Wales.

Blaenavon Ironworks had been set up with astonishing speed. In little more than five years, the three partners had invested £40,000 to create this vast new enterprise. However, two of them did not live to see their investment come to fruition. Hopkins died in 1793 and Pratt in 1794. Thomas Hill and his nephew, Samuel Hopkins (1762–1815), were left in control.

The Growth of a Community 1800–36

By the turn of the new century, Blaenavon Ironworks was a success and south Wales was the foremost iron-producing region in the world, surpassing both Shropshire and Staffordshire in output. Demand for iron was high during the French wars (1793–1815) and Hill and Hopkins decided to invest further. In 1800 they ordered a new blowing engine from the firm of Boulton & Watt that could provide sufficient blast for another two furnaces. The yard was extended and one new furnace was added in 1801 (Furnace 4) and another in 1807 (Furnace 5). These furnaces were soon served by yet another engine, built in 1819. The partners also extended their mineral workings to the deeper seams in the valley,

sinking Engine Pit in 1806, from which coal was raised with the aid of waterwheels.

The ironmasters turned their attention to their lack of manufacturing capacity by developing forges for converting pigs into the more valuable wrought iron (pp. 44, 54). Around 1804 they seem to have collaborated in constructing Cwmavon forge, beside their tramroad down the valley. Then, in 1817–18, they reorientated their export route and built a substantial forge, together with a new community, on the mountain top at Garnddyrys. This was part of a programme of work developed by Thomas Hill II (1767–1827), who had become managing partner and taken over Samuel Hopkins's quarter share after his death in 1815. It included the construction of a plateway tramroad from Blaenavon, through Garnddyrys, to the newly completed Brecknock & Abergavenny Canal, which offered lower tolls to Newport than the Monmouthshire Canal. This

Hill's tramroad winding its way as a level path around the Tumble, between Pwll-du and Garnddyrys. The tramroad was built by Thomas Hill II (1767–1827) in 1817–18 to link the ironworks to the Brecknock & Abergavenny Canal at Llanfoist. The route climbing steeply up the hill is the ancient road Rhiw Ifor. A tramroad branch dropping to Pwll-du quarry can be made out between this and the level tramroad.

The early iron-making community, depicted by the mine agent, Thomas Deakin, in his 'Plan of the Tram Road from Blaenavon Furnaces to Pwll Dee, and Garn dydrys' of 1819. The blast furnaces and their cast houses are numbered one to five. The snaking lines of two mineral outcrops have been marked, as has Engine Pit with its water-power ponds. Workers' houses are thrown wherever they are needed, near the ironworks and spread around the mines. A town as such does not yet exist, but the church, school and manager's house (enclosed by green fields) have been erected along the line of the 'Rail Road to Ponty Pool', and there is another cluster of buildings near the Nonconformists' 'New Meeting House'. Most of the tramroads are not marked, but the recently built 'Tram Road from the Furnaces to the Tunnel Mouth' curves around from the ironworks yard and through the mountain toward Pwll-du, while another line of it brings limestone to the furnace tops. A major watercourse, of 1801, comes from the Afon Lwyd across a recently infilled valley as a 'Feeder to the Engines' (Gwent Record Office).

Below: Thomas Deakin's iron-topped tomb in Blaenavon churchyard. Deakin worked underground in Shropshire as a child, and came to Blaenavon aged 22 in 1798, where he became mine agent. The inscription was written by Deakin: 'Beneath the rocks I used to toil for bread, Beneath this rock I rest my weary head…'.

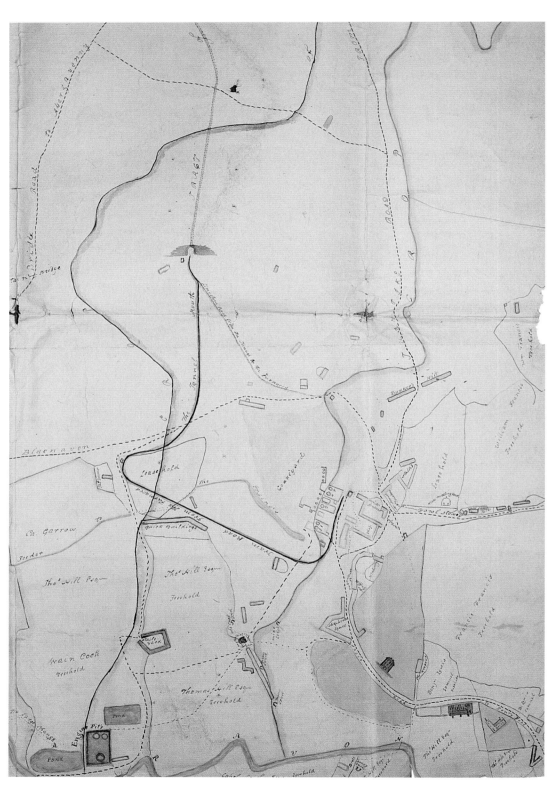

reorientation of the export route also helped the company to diversify into selling coal and lime inland. Hill's tramroad took a dramatic route through the longest tramroad tunnel ever to have been built, along the steep slopes of the Blorenge, and down a series of counterbalanced inclines to the canal at Llanfoist.

In the early nineteenth century Blaenavon was still a scattered settlement rather than a town (albeit larger than Cardiff), but a nucleus had begun to evolve around the ironworks and the tramroad towards Pontypool. Thomas Deakin's map of 1819 shows the cluster of terraces near the works and, below this, the mansion built for Samuel Hopkins between 1798 and 1800. Close by are the Anglican church built by Hopkins and Hill for the new community in 1804 and St Peter's School of 1816. Many of the immigrants to Blaenavon, as in other industrial communities, brought with them Nonconformist religion: the Baptists, who met initially in a farmhouse, built Horeb Chapel in 1807, and the Calvinistic Methodists replaced their early chapel with a 'New Meeting House' in 1819 — shown to the right of the ironworks on Deakin's map. By 1833 there were 430 houses owned by the company, and 1,000 workers.

Early nineteenth-century Blaenavon suffered from the boom-and-bust economy that was a cause of strife throughout the iron-making districts, where all livelihoods depended on the health of trade. The price of iron plummeted after the end of the French wars in 1815, and there were savage wage cuts. Many ironworkers went on strike and furnaces were put out. Depression hit again in 1821–22, when the Blaenavon colliers struck and there were running battles with troops. Among the manifestations of unrest in the region were the 'Scotch Cattle', a secret society of strikers disguised with cloaks and horns who terrorized those continuing to work. Dissatisfaction was deepened by the workers' dependence on the ironmasters for their housing and their credit at the company shops, and there were growing calls for common men to have the vote. The crescendo was the Merthyr Rising of 1831, during which the workers for the first time flew the red flag (later to become the symbol of socialism) and the military had to rescue the besieged ironmasters. At least sixteen people were killed in battles in the centre of Merthyr Tydfil. Troops were also called out at Blaenavon at various times. Depression produced a wave of emigration — in 1832 seventy people set off on just one ship from Newport to Philadelphia.

Thomas Hill II had become virtual sole owner of the works on his father's death in 1824, but he died only three years later and his 39-year-old son took over the Blaenavon empire. As in many industrial families, the third generation had different interests: Thomas Hill III (1798–1868) had been educated at Eton and Oxford and preferred the life of a country gentleman. He bought a mansion 30 miles (48km) away at Rudhall, Ross-on-Wye, and sought to auction the iron company in 1833. It failed to reach the reserve. Hill decided instead to convert the enterprise to a joint stock company, retaining a seat on the board under the chairmanship of a London iron merchant, William Unwin Sims (d. 1839). The Blaenavon Iron Company was launched in 1836.

Above: Great House, now The Beeches, was built for Samuel Hopkins between 1798 and 1800 (RCAHMW). It is encircled by a wall capped with iron slag (below).

Iron production at Blaenavon Ironworks 1796–1858

Year	No of furnaces	Annual output in tons
1796	3	4,318
1805	4 (3 in blast)	7,846
1823	5	16,882
1830	5	13,843
1858	5	26,872

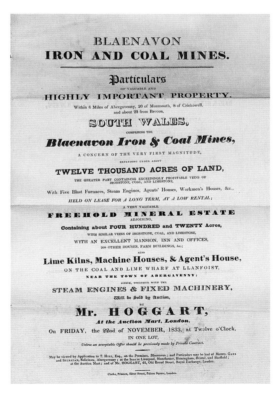

The prospectus for Blaenavon Ironworks when Thomas Hill III (1798–1868) put it up for auction unsuccessfully in 1833 (Gwent Record Office).

The industrial strife of iron-making communities was among the factors that made south Wales sympathetic to political radicalism. In the late 1830s there was considerable support for the Chartists, who sought a series of democratic reforms in the government of the nation. Some 5,000 Chartists marched on Newport from several of the Monmouthshire ironworks on 3 and 4 November 1839. Men set off from Blaenavon but turned back owing to bad weather. The march ended in disaster when troops opened fire on the demonstrators, killing at least twenty. The leaders of what seemed like a revolution were sentenced to transportation (National Library of Wales).

Victorian Reorganizations 1836–70

As the young Princess Victoria was about to ascend the throne, an optimistic new era of reorganization was beginning at Blaenavon Ironworks. It was led by the new managing director, James Ashwell (1799–1881), the son of a Nottinghamshire ironmaster, who had studied Classics at Edinburgh University. 1836 was a boom year and Ashwell began investing in the ironworks, new mines and houses. The key was the development of a new works, to be called Forgeside, on a pocket of freehold land not owned by Lord Abergavenny, which the Hills had acquired on the other side of the valley. With the new works, the company would be much less at the mercy of the rents, royalties and insecurity of the leasehold.

Ashwell laid the foundations for new blast furnaces, forges and rolling mills, but the new era proved to be a false dawn. The industry experienced a sharp downturn into what would be called 'The Hungry Forties', and there was a catalogue of disasters: a flood at one of the company's pits in 1838 killed fifteen; Sims, the company's chairman, shot himself in 1839; and in the same year political unrest boiled over in

the Chartist uprising at Newport. Ashwell had spent £138,000, yet there was little profit in sight. Absentee shareholders did not have the long-term vision that had informed earlier proprietors, and they were horrified by the expenditure. Ashwell resigned on New Year's Day 1841. With hindsight, whilst his architectural tastes were costly (the grandiose balance tower, pp. 26–28, and formal terraces of housing), his investments would in due course have paid off. As it was, the Forgeside development was abandoned.

Nevertheless, the 1840s saw the scattered settlement of Blaenavon at last begin to be a town. A new centre grew up on privately owned plots (it was not a 'company town' despite the Blaenavon Iron Company's influence over the lives of most inhabitants). Broad Street evolved from 1840 and chapels, shops, public houses and new dwellings colonized it quickly.

As so often in the iron towns of Wales, good times — characterized by cash in workers' pockets and booming retail trade — alternated with repossessions, unrest and emigration. In August 1843, it was reported that sheriff's officers carrying away the goods of Samuel Deakin were 'attacked by several hundred persons, men, women, and children: most of the men had their faces blackened'. Placards were put

The town of Blaenavon gradually developed during the course of the 1840s. The Bethlehem Independent Chapel, constructed in 1840, was one of many erected during that decade.

up warning the officers not to show themselves in Blaenavon again 'or their lives would be sacrificed'. A five per cent wage cut in 1847 brought a three-month strike and in 1848 *The Monmouthshire Merlin* reported that: 'From forty to fifty souls left this place for America last week, and others are preparing to follow them.' Skilled Blaenavon emigrants were moving overseas to work with industrial competitors, while the workforce was replenished by immigrants from England and Ireland.

Much of the infrastructure of the works, so up to date when it was built, was now half a century old. The modernization process was led, in spite of anxious shareholders, by the new chairman, R. W. Kennard (1800–70), a Scottish ironmaster whose family was to dominate the company for nearly a century. The managers, Harry Scrivenor and Richard Johnson, sank Hill Pits in 1843–44 and introduced coke ovens to reduce the waste from burning coal in heaps. Around 1850 they brought in standard-gauge rail lines and two steam locomotives to replace some of the company's hundreds of horses. Four years later the old horse-drawn 'Blaenavon Railroad' was relaid for steam operation as part of a railway built by the Monmouthshire Canal proprietors, giving direct access to the quay at Newport.

The international rail boom was the driving force behind the growth of business. Thousands of miles of railway were opening up the continents, using south Wales iron. From the 1840s to the 1870s Blaenavon concentrated almost exclusively on the production of rails, with orders coming from England, Brazil, India, Russia and other countries across the globe. However, the Kennards also promoted structural projects, supplying cast iron for Blackfriars Bridge in London and Crumlin Viaduct and developing a novel product: corrugated-iron sheets.

Ashwell's unfinished Forgeside works must have seemed a ghostly presence for two decades after it was abandoned, but the development was finally resumed: the puddling forge opened in 1859 and engines were bought for rolling mills in 1860. Garnddyrys forge was closed in 1863 and the village that had clung to the mountain top for a generation was gradually deserted. At the ironworks itself a new blowing-engine house was built — with a smart corrugated-iron roof and boilers heated by waste gas — and the first new furnace for half a century went into blast (Furnace 6). It was decided at last to go ahead with large, modern furnaces at Forgeside, using preheated blast air to save fuel: three were working by 1869 and were capable of two or three times the output of their earlier counterparts. Forgeside was already an enormous enterprise, serviced by seventy-two coke ovens, seventy-two puddling furnaces, and numerous mills and engines.

Below left: Crumlin Viaduct under construction. All the wrought iron for the innovative trusses was rolled at Blaenavon and fabricated at the Kennards' own Crumlin works, while castings for the piers, which were 200 feet (61m) high, came from Kennard's works at Falkirk in Scotland. Work began in 1853 and the railway opened in 1857. The viaduct was demolished in 1966 (National Monuments Record of Wales: Bernard Howarth-Loomes Collection).

Below: The Forgeside works in 1896. Three circular blast furnaces are shown (with pierced parapets) and four hot-blast stoves. The furnace on the right is constructed of firebricks bound with iron bands, and the other two are clad with plates (National Museum of Wales).

Above: Sir Henry Bessemer (1813–98) opened the new era of mild steel production with his invention of the Bessemer Converter in 1856 (British Library).

Below right: Many ironworks in south Wales closed after the 1860s in the face of competition from the new bulk steel industry. This photograph of the ruined Penydarren works in Merthyr Tydfil, taken about 1870 by Robert Thompson Crawshay (1817–79), the Cyfarthfa ironmaster, hints at the shock that many people in the industry must have felt (National Museum of Wales).

Below: E. P. Martin (1844–1910), general manager of the Blaenavon company from 1874 until 1882, when he moved on to be general manager at Dowlais. Martin was responsible for beginning steel production at Blaenavon and helped Sidney Gilchrist Thomas (1850–85) with his experiments (Jane E. Cresswell).

The company, like the rest of south Wales, was fighting to keep up with the increasing international competition and was having to import ore to supplement the depleting local supplies. The region might have a hundred times the output of the 1780s — with 169 furnaces in operation at forty-eight sites in 1854 — but growth was levelling off. The biggest challenge came from the invention of the Bessemer process, which enabled the conversion of pig iron into a superior material — mild steel — with a carbon content between that of cast and wrought iron. Although steel had been known as an exceptionally hard-wearing and malleable alloy for tools and weapons since the Iron Age, it could only be produced by intensive, small-scale methods. The process invented by Henry Bessemer (1813–98) in 1856 enabled cheap steel to be made in bulk in a 'converter' by blowing air through molten pig iron to remove carbon and impurities. The enormous ironworks at Dowlais and Ebbw Vale took up the new technology quickly. Briefly, in the 1860s, south Wales became the leading steel producer in the world. However, the iron companies were labouring against a major problem: the pig iron they produced from the local iron ore was rich in phosphorus. This made steel that was brittle, and they were forced to rely on costly imported ores. Yet the greater durability of Bessemer steel for rails was incontestable; by 1880 British production of wrought-iron rails would slump to a tenth of what it was in 1870. Blaenavon had to modernize or die.

Steel and Coal 1870–1918

The company was relaunched as the Blaenavon Iron & Steel Company in 1870 and its new general manager, E. P. Martin (1844–1910), set about investing in steel. Blaenavon was to be one of only six south Wales ironworks that succeeded in making the change. Two large Bessemer converters were built at Forgeside by 1877. Ore was brought from Northamptonshire, Cumbria and Spain, mostly by sail to Newport and up the valley by train, reducing the profit margin considerably. The company's coal mines, limestone quarries and brickyards were all hard at work and the blast furnaces were busy making pig iron to be converted into steel ingots. These were rolled to make rails or taken to the specialist 'tyre' mill. The old works was still producing some cold-blast iron for the market as well as pig for Forgeside, and had a busy foundry making cast-iron objects for local use. Additional blast furnaces were built at both sites. In 1878 the company employed 5,000 people. However, it had overreached itself financially and failed amid the tough competition of the late 1870s, as works after works across south Wales closed down for good.

Given the obstacle to using phosphoric local ores in steelmaking it was ironic that Sir Henry Bessemer carried out his successful experiments for the converter with pig iron from Blaenavon. It appeared that he had used a batch that happened to be low in

Sidney Gilchrist Thomas

Sidney Gilchrist Thomas (1850–85) came from a Welsh family and grew up in London. As a young man he was fascinated by chemistry and at the age of 19 he set himself to make steel with the phosphoric ores that could not be used in Bessemer converters, realizing that to do so would bring fame and fortune. He experimented in his spare time from his work as a clerk at the Metropolitan Police Courts. When his cousin, Percy Carlyle Gilchrist (1851–1935), was appointed as Blaenavon works' chemist in 1876 they began to work together in great secrecy, Thomas travelling down from London to Blaenavon every Friday night and returning on Sunday. The general manager of the works, E. P. Martin, got wind of their activities and said: 'It is evident that you young men have some secret experimental work on hand; do you not think it would be well if you took me into your confidence?' As a result, the company made available a small Bessemer converter for their experiments. In 1878 they announced that they had eliminated phosphorus by lining the converter with dolomitic limestone bricks. The process was perfected in Middlesborough in 1879, after the collapse of the Blaenavon company. The 'basic Bessemer' or 'Thomas' process significantly advanced steelmaking in countries like Germany and the United States of America, where phosphoric ores were abundant, and created a slag fertilizer that was to be used world-wide. Thomas saw some of his success, but he died aged 35. The American steel magnate, Andrew Carnegie, wrote, 'These two young men, Thomas and Gilchrist of Blaenavon, did more for Britain's greatness than all the Kings and Queens put together.'

A memorial to Sidney Gilchrist Thomas that was unveiled at the Forgeside works in 1960. It now stands near the entrance to Blaenavon Ironworks.

Left: A chalk portrait of Sidney Gilchrist Thomas by an unknown artist (National Portrait Gallery, London).

phosphorous, perhaps made from imported haematite, leading him to overlook the problem. However, in 1878 Blaenavon was also part of the solution that allowed the use of phosphoric iron ore, discovered by Sidney Gilchrist Thomas (1850–85) and Percy Carlyle Gilchrist (1851–1935) through experiments at the works. The company was allowed to use the 'basic Bessemer' or 'Thomas' process without paying royalties. Unfortunately, the discovery provided vital stimulation to steel production in Germany and North America, which also had phosphoric ores — but almost untapped mineral reserves. Within four years, fourteen works around Europe had invested in the process and a consortium of steelmakers, led by the American steel magnate, Andrew Carnegie, had paid $250,000 to use it in the United States of America.

Given the increasing difficulties of competition, many south Wales iron companies expanded their coal-mining interests, and some, which did not enter the steel business, became dedicated coal companies. Good steam coal was now in high demand to fuel stationary engines, locomotives and steamships, and the south Wales coalfield exported more than any other in the world, with markets in the Mediterranean, South America, Africa and the Far East. In 1880, the Blaenavon company opened Big Pit (p.62) and increased the output from its other collieries to become one of the largest producers in the coalfield. Blaenavon coal was used by the Great Western Railway and was shipped regularly to South America. When coal production in south Wales reached its peak in 1913 there were over 500 working collieries and the industry employed a quarter of a million people.

The later nineteenth century brought improving social conditions. A hospital for the treatment of

The boom time in steam coal exports from south Wales is expressed in the imagery of trains and steamships on the Pierhead Building in Cardiff Bay, built in 1896–97. It bears the motto, 'Wrth ddwr a than' — 'By water and fire' (Photolibrary Wales).

Right: Colliers worked in claustrophobic conditions in the narrow coal seams. This photograph of about 1905 shows a man undercutting the coal to make it fall, working by the light of a naked candle. It was taken by W. E. Jones at a level in Pontypool (National Museum of Wales).

Blaenavon Workmen's Hall and Institute opened in 1895. Of the total cost of £10,000, £9,000 was raised by the workmen, who also contributed voluntary labour. It was designed by the Newport architect, E. A. Lansdowne.

accidents was built at Blaenavon in 1883, managed by a committee of workers and agents of the company. The twelve-hour working day was reduced to nine in 1872, giving greater time for social activities and, for the miner, the opportunity to see daylight on more days of the year. Blaenavon had three choirs, a string orchestra, three brass bands and five dramatic societies, all extra to the musical and theatrical activities of the chapels. In 1882 the workmen of Blaenavon set up a committee to establish an institute, contributing a halfpenny a week from their wages. The Blaenavon Workmen's Hall and Institute was an extraordinary new focus for education when

it opened in 1895, containing meeting rooms and club rooms, a library, and an auditorium to seat 1,500. By 1912 its library was taking sixty different newspapers a week, plus twenty-two monthly magazines and six evening papers. Over a hundred such institutes were built in Wales between the 1880s and the 1930s. The town continued to grow in population, peaking in 1921 with some 13,000 people. Many new streets were added, and an 1891 directory identified eighteen places of worship.

The vital American market for British steel was virtually closed when the protectionist McKinley tariffs were introduced in 1890, made possible by the contribution of the Thomas process to American self-sufficiency. By 1902 Britain had slipped to third place in international steel production, after Germany and the USA. A catastrophic series of strikes and lockouts at Blaenavon from 1900 to 1904 led hundreds of people to leave for good. The furnaces at the old ironworks were blown-out, bringing to an end a 215-year history of smelting at the site.

When Forgeside started up again, the old works became a maintenance depot, its large foundry and workshops remaining busy and employing 170 people. Crucially for future conservationists, this saved the site from the disuse or redevelopment that resulted in the clearance of most other ironworks throughout the country. The most significant damage was that done in 1911 when stone was robbed to build St James's Church.

The company produced good profits in 1908 and invested in open-hearth furnaces for steel making in 1909, but the plant was soon struggling to compete. It closed in 1911, making 500 redundant, reopening only for the duration of the First World War to make munitions. The company concentrated instead on coal production, coke making, and gas by-products.

Decline and Rebirth in the Twentieth Century

The iron furnaces and steelworks restarted briefly in 1924–25, but few heavy industrial enterprises were sustainable at this time. The whole of south Wales was hit terribly by the Great Depression, the impact of which was amplified by the rapid decline in demand for steam coal as ships turned to oil fuel.

In 1927 unemployment at Blaenavon was over forty per cent. Robert Kennard, the last of his family to be involved with Blaenavon, died in 1929, and in 1934 much of the Forgeside plant was sold for scrap. Investment was found for a new steel plant in 1937, in readiness for the ensuing war, and it operated until 1948. However, there were no blast furnaces left to service the works. It would have been unbelievable to previous generations, but Blaenavon now had to bring pig iron from elsewhere.

During the Second World War, opencast mines were started at Pwll-du to fuel steamships brought back into service for the war effort (p. 53); then in 1947 the nationalization of the coal industry took place, bringing some much needed new investment to Big Pit. The old ironworks site continued in use as a small-scale engineering workshop and coal yard until the 1960s, while part of the Forgeside site was redeveloped by Daniel Doncaster & Sons to manufacture specialist steel parts, particularly for aircraft, keeping the tradition of metalworking alive. With so many jobs lost, however, the population of Blaenavon inevitably declined, reaching around 6,000 — less than half its former peak.

For many, Blaenavon was a depressing scene, but it inspired the novelist Alexander Cordell (1914–97) to research and write his historical novel, *The Rape of the Fair Country* (1959), which was set in Blaenavon and Garnddyrys at the height of the Industrial Revolution (p. 61). At about the same time, industrial archaeology began to emerge as a discipline and interest in conservation began to grow. In 1964, conscious of the continuing demolition of disused structures, T. B. Parry wrote in the brand new *Journal of Industrial Archaeology*, 'Before it is too late on the Blorenge and elsewhere there is much to be recorded by the industrial archaeologist.' This was early recognition of Blaenavon as one of the most important industrial archaeological sites in Britain.

Nevertheless, attitudes to the relics of industrialization remained strongly negative. Much of the earliest industrial housing was cleared: Staffordshire Row, North Street and Shepherd Square, on the doorstep of the ironworks, were all considered unsuitable for continued use and were not yet recognized as worthy of conservation. Pwll-du village was demolished too. The ironworks itself was due for clearance in a land reclamation scheme, but in 1970 proposals for its conservation led to the

establishment of a Blaenavon Research Committee, and negotiations began the next year to take the site into State care. In 1974 the painstaking conservation of the ironworks began.

When Big Pit was due to close as a working mine in 1980, arrangements were already in place for it to become a museum, and it opened to the public in 1983. Statutory protection was provided for various sites in and around Blaenavon, ranging from well-preserved sections of tramroad to shops and public buildings in the town.

The latest transformation of Blaenavon came in November 2000, when it achieved World Heritage status. The inscription stated: 'The area around Blaenavon bears eloquent and exceptional testimony to the pre-eminence of south Wales as the world's major producer of iron and coal in the nineteenth century. All the necessary elements can be seen in situ — coal and ore mines, quarries, a primitive railway system, furnaces, the homes of the workers, and the social infrastructure of their community.' Today, the ironworks are cared for by Cadw, the historic environment service of the Welsh Assembly Government. Big Pit has been reinvigorated as the National Coal Museum, and the town and landscape are managed by partners who work together to ensure that the extraordinary story of Blaenavon and its people can continue to be told to future generations.

Blaenavon Ironworks in ruins in the 1960s, before the beginning of conservation work in 1974.

Son et lumière *at Blaenavon Ironworks.*

A Tour of Blaenavon Ironworks

This tour suggests a route around all the main features of Blaenavon Ironworks, but they can be visited in any order using the ground plan below or the bird's-eye view at the front of the guidebook. The numbers next to the headings in the tour correspond to those on the bird's-eye view. The tour begins at the viewpoint that overlooks the furnace yard partway up the slope, near the cottages.

At each point on the tour, the first section of the guide (highlighted in green) explains the key features to be seen. This is followed by more detailed descriptions and historical background which you may prefer to read after your visit.

Above: A sixpenny token from the Blaenavon truck shop (National Museum of Wales).

Opposite: The stone towers of Furnace 4 and Furnace 5 at Blaenavon Ironworks, encasing the yellow firebrick of the linings, standing against the cliff cut away to create the furnace yard (pp. 38–40). The outer stonework was robbed to build a church in 1911. The low walls in front mark the former cast houses where the molten iron ran out, while wagons of hot slag were carried away on the curving railway line.

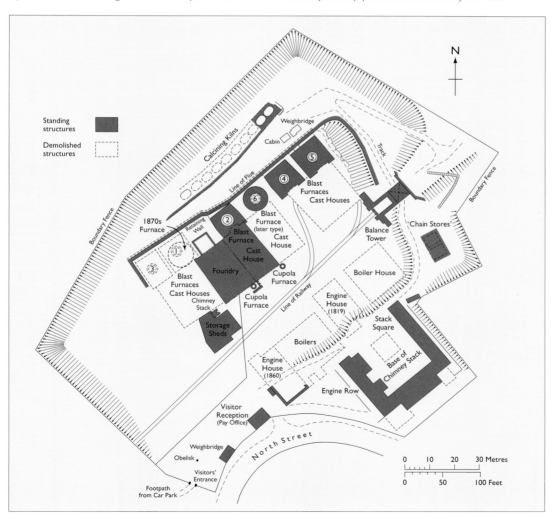

Please keep within the demarcated public areas: conservation continues and parts of the site are dangerous. Areas accessible to the public may vary.

N

Visitors'
Entrance

Viewpoint Over the Yard

This yard was once the beating heart of the surrounding landscape. From 1789 to 1900 it teemed with activity day and night around streams of molten iron. Sir Richard Colt Hoare sketched here when Blaenavon Ironworks was just a decade old and already one of the largest and most advanced operations in the world. In the twentieth century the works became a maintenance depot and it was in ruins when conservation began in 1974. Today, it is the most complete ironworks of its date and type in the world. All the components of an Industrial Revolution ironworks are visible. The high charging bank was where iron ore, coal and limestone were assembled and the ore was roasted in calcining kilns. The furnaces were built against a hillside cut back to a vertical face. Molten iron was tapped at their base and run out into cast houses, one of which still stands in front of Furnace 2, to the right of a foundry for casting iron objects. Also in the yard are the foundations for blast engines which pumped air to the furnaces; and dominating the whole ironworks is the balance tower, which raised wagons to the upper level. Close by are key workers' cottages.

Ironmasters set up new works all along the rim of the south Wales coalfield, bringing the latest methods of the Industrial Revolution to places rich in the essential raw materials for iron making: iron ore, coal and limestone. The promoters of Blaenavon Ironworks arrived from the Midlands to acquire a vast landholding, stretching as far as you can see. The location of the works, high above the river, shows their confidence in the new technology of blowing by steam engine. Earlier furnaces had been built close to sure supplies of water for waterwheels to power the blast reliably. But here, if the blowing engine broke down, the furnace contents would become a solid, useless mass.

Unlike previous ironmasters, who had developed works gradually, they built three furnaces straight away: the right-hand furnace in Colt Hoare's watercolour still stands at the middle of the site, behind the cast house (Furnace 2). By the time of his visit the ironworks employed some 350 people and produced perhaps 5,000 tons of iron a year. Two more furnaces (Furnaces 4 and 5) were added to the right soon afterwards. Although the yard was orientated for smoke to be taken away by the wind, it often filled with fumes. Many who came seeking work must have been astonished to encounter a new world of industry and elemental forces, and probably the largest structures they had ever seen.

Engine Row ◆2

The first two cottages in Engine Row have been reinstated — one furnished to suggest the home of a foreman in 1790 and the other as it might have been for a labouring family half a century later. The other cottages contain an exhibition and models of the site and surrounding landscape. The houses were built around 1788 to attract key personnel to help establish the ironworks on this barren moorland. Seen through their eyes, they would have been comfortable and spacious. Engine Row was lived in until the 1960s, and is a rare surviving example of early iron company housing.

These cottages were a great improvement over the one-room hovels of many rural labourers, or the typical one-up, one-down houses of industrial workers. They helped lure expert staff from established ironworks. They were built of local stone and limewashed against the weather. The terraced plan and the brick arches were typical of Midlands-style workers' houses, but the oak roofs and staircases followed local carpentry traditions. The roof was covered originally with split sandstone (pieces have been found in excavations), and only later with slate. The first windows were probably wooden casements with leaded glazing, but sashes were installed in the 1860s. Surviving sills hint at the use at some point of non-opening iron frames, common in ironworkers' housing by the early nineteenth century, so these were chosen for the restoration. The doors had an outward-opening

Left: Sir Richard Colt Hoare's watercolour of Blaenavon Ironworks when it was only a few years old, an engraving of which was published in William Coxe's An Historical Tour in Monmouthshire *in 1801. On the horizon are charging houses, where materials were prepared to be tipped into the furnaces. Three blast furnaces stand against the rear of the yard, with their casting houses stretching out in front and the blowing-engine house between (with two round chimneys). To the right, Colt Hoare saw a coal level running under the hillside and a cliff being cut away where two more furnaces were shortly to be built. On the left of the yard there appear to be two reverberatory furnaces for remelting iron, and a pile of pigs and scrap. The elevated walkway may have taken a water trough to the steam boilers and been used for delivering coal to the boilers or sand to the pig beds: a woman crossing it has a basket on her head. Coxe said that Colt Hoare drew here on their joint visit in August 1798, but he appears to have visited earlier also, between 1792 and 1795 (© Yale Centre for British Art, Paul Mellon Collection, USA/ Bridgeman Art Library).*

Top: In the same view today, two of the furnaces have gone, but the one to the right still remains.

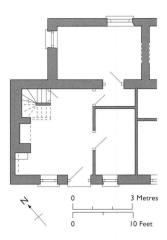

Above: The ground-floor plan of No. 1 Engine Row. The living room, with its open fire for cooking, has a bedroom and a pantry positioned off it and a staircase behind the chimney breast. A thin wall separates it from No. 2. A later extension was accessed through the pantry.

Right: A reconstruction of Engine Row in the mid-nineteenth century (Illustration by Geraint Derbyshire).

Above: The Morgan brothers outside their house in Engine Row shortly before the First World War. The outward-opening half-door is visible.

bottom leaf, with a full-length inner door behind. The full-length door could be left open to allow ventilation and the half-door closed to shut out sheep and keep small children from the dangers of the ironworks. None of the cottages had gardens; and there would have been not grass but ash and cinder all around them.

Inside, there were flagstones (an improvement on earth floors), lath partitions, whitewashed walls and plank doors. The living room, with an open grate for cooking, would have been furnished by the first generation who lived here probably with an oak table, chairs, wooden stools for children, a cupboard or dresser, and perhaps a settle or bench. Also downstairs were a larder and a small bedroom — a luxury in giving parents a private sleeping place. Another room was added later at the back. A curving staircase against the chimney breast — of typical Welsh style — led to two bedrooms open to the roof. These would have been furnished with no more than straw mattresses on the floor. Lighting was by rushlights or candles. There was no water supply and, until communal toilets were built in the late nineteenth century, people used ash buckets and emptied them outside.

We know something of the people who lived in the Blaenavon houses — most probably in Engine Row — from the census of 1841. By this time the key staff had moved to other dwellings. One cottage was occupied by the Hartshorn family — Emanuel, who worked on the coke heaps, his wife, their two small children, and a girl who was probably a lodger. The family came from Wednesbury in Staffordshire in the 1830s, and by 1850 had emigrated to the emerging iron industry of Pennsylvania. In the next house lived nine people: Timothy McCarthy, who worked filling the furnaces, his wife, two boys who also worked at the ironworks (p. 31), three younger children and a related couple. Such crowding was not unusual. Eight people lived in the next cottage and nine in that beyond.

Stack Square ◆3

Visitors' Entrance

This courtyard was built with Engine Row around 1788. It came to be known as Stack Square after the chimney constructed in the middle of it about 1860, which loomed 144 feet (44m) above the cottages (almost twice the height of the balance tower). The chimney was partially demolished in about 1905, but its base can still be seen. North Row, parallel to Engine Row, also had double-fronted houses. The middle range contained the company shop, offices and a house for the works' manager before it was converted to cottages.

Addresses were informal in this fast-growing township. The square was known successively as Office Square, Engine Square, Late Shop Square, Old Shop Square, Stack Square, Big Stack Square and Shop Square. Company shops were critical to new iron-making communities, though they were causes of unrest (p. 26). Originally, the shop, manager's house and offices took up equal sections of the middle row. By 1814 the whole row had become the shop, and had been extended backwards. The roof oversailed the old rear wall and rafters, and the windows were blocked up. Buildings also projected into the square and part of the shop had a lower storey. However, in

Below: The enormous chimney in Stack Square, in about 1900. Its scale can be judged by the glimpse of the whitewashed front of Engine Row. The chimney drew waste gas from the furnaces across the yard and into the boilers for the engine houses, and was probably built at the same time as the last blowing-engine house in 1860. This is visible to the left, with its curving corrugated-iron roof, its blast pipe leaving the gable, and steam rising from the boilers. The taller engine house of 1819 is behind. On the right of the photograph are the company's workshops (National Museum of Wales).

Above: One of the reconstructed doors on Middle Row at Blaenavon. The full-length inner door could be left open for ventilation while the outer half-door was closed to protect small children from the dangers in the ironworks and to prevent sheep from wandering in.

Above: Exterior of the Rhyd-y-car terrace now at the National History Museum, St Fagans, Cardiff. The houses were built in about 1800 for workers at Richard Crawshay's Ynysfach Ironworks at Merthyr Tydfil (National Museum of Wales).

Right: The interior of one of the Rhyd-y-car houses furnished as it might have been in 1855 (National Museum of Wales).

Life in the Cottages

A rare description of the interiors of iron company houses, in Merthyr Tydfil, was published in *The Morning Chronicle*, 1849–51. Industrial employment brought a wealth of new possessions in the mid-nineteenth century.

'The houses of the workmen are built in rows of uniform height and size. They are of three classes. The best are two stories, have four small sash windows (which, by the way, are never opened), two above and one each side of the door. On the ground floor there is a roomy kitchen with a stone floor; adjoining is a small room, just large enough to contain a four-post bed, a chest of drawers, a small corner cupboard, two chairs, a window table, which usually form its contents. The ceiling is not plastered, and the rafters are used for hanging up the crockery and the household utensils. Above stairs are two bedrooms, one large and the other small; the ceiling here is of lath and plaster. This is all, except, perhaps a narrow cupboard cut off from the lower bedroom, and dignified with the name of 'pantry'. There is no strip of garden, no backdoor or outlet, no place of accommodation, no drain to carry away house refuse, nor any pump or pipe for the supply of water. The street in front is consequently made the receptacle of every kind of abomination conceivable.

Such are the residences of the best class of workmen in and around Merthyr. These houses are, for the most part, the very type of cleanliness and order. They are stuffed with furniture even to superfluity; a fine mahogany eight-day clock, a showy mahogany chest of drawers, a set of mahogany chairs with solid seats, a glass-fronted cupboard for the display of china, glass and silver spoons, forming indispensable requisites for the principal room. The other apartments are equally well furnished. The habits of the women with respect of their houses, are those of cleanliness, decency and order. They are always scrubbing the rooms, polishing and regulating the furniture, or with long brushes are laying white or yellow washes upon the front of their houses.' (from Eurwyn Wiliam, *Rhyd-y-car: A Welsh Mining Community*, 1987).

the mid-nineteenth century the shop was moved across North Street and the middle row was converted to one-room-wide houses by making new dividing walls and repositioning doors and windows, as the patched façade bears witness. It was probably at around this time that the square was reroofed in north Wales slate and fitted with sash windows.

The houses in North Row were the largest in Stack Square. Two had fireplaces in both downstairs rooms — creating separate parlours and kitchens — and they were a third bigger than the cottages in Engine Row. They had back doors into a passage behind, and rear windows upstairs.

By 1840, the company had built 500 houses to accommodate the families who flooded into the area, and even more were provided later. At the ironworks itself, Chain Square (alias Iron Street) once extended uphill from the corner of North Row, a pair of cottages stood at the base of the balance tower, and a back-to-back block stood in the yard, part of which became the offices.

Just above Stack Square, the enigmatic arched structures beside the path to the upper yard are known as the 'chain stores'. In 1843 they were said to be smiths' shops, and they may have specialized in making chains.

Above: Engine Row, with Stack Square behind. Built in 1788 to house key workers for the new ironworks, it was laid out to a Midlands pattern and provided high-quality accommodation for its time. The three-storey section was part of the company shop in Stack Square.

Left: The base of the chimney that gave Stack Square its name, surrounded by the north and middle terraces and Engine Row (RCAHMW).

Left: The arched 'chain stores', once used as smiths' shops.

Company Shops and the Truck System

Company shops ('truck' or 'tommy' shops) were vital to new industrial communities. They sold a comprehensive range of goods: when the Blaenavon shop moved to North Street it had bakehouses, grocery and drapery counters, a meat room and a slaughter house, a butter room, flour room, cheese room, boot and shoe room and a public house. They were lucrative — the Blaenavon shops in the 1830s provided a tenth of the company's profits. However, abuses of such monopolies were blamed for social unrest. There were complaints that goods were overpriced and poor, while debtors were dealt with

The minute book of the Blaenavon Iron Company records profits made by the company shops at Blaenavon and Pwll-du in 1839 (Gwent Record Office, D. 751.356).

unjustly. The Merthyr Rising of 1831 was sparked by the calling-in of shop debts at a time of pay cuts.

The 'truck' system, whereby workers were effectively paid not in money but in goods from the company shop, was especially divisive. It was said that truck provided a man with his cradle and his coffin, and half starved him in between. The law asserted that workers should be paid in coin of the realm, but even after the Truck Acts of 1831 and 1887 there were loopholes (and the employers were often the magistrates). Only a few ironmasters paid wages in their own token coinage (tokens for the Blaenavon shop appear to have been used only for change). However, the system of 'long pay', paying wages after four or six weeks, was widespread. Few families had savings, so they had to use the company shop, where debts could be deducted from future pay. They were in almost perpetual debt to the company, and tied to their jobs. Such abuses provided an impetus to alternative provision. In Blaenavon, this occurred from the 1840s as a town centre grew up on one of the few plots of land not controlled by the ironmasters (pp. 12, 47–50). A co-operative store was opened in 1861.

The Balance Tower

The balance tower was a lift to connect the lower and upper yards, powered by the weight of water. It is the main architectural feature of the ironworks, built around 1839 by the Classically-educated manager, James Ashwell, who was criticized by the shareholders for overspending (p. 12). Although it is rubble masonry at the rear, the dressed stonework at the front was designed to impress. The lift raised wagons 80 feet (25m) to the upper yard. It may have been intended primarily to take raw materials, which increasingly were brought from across the valley, to the furnace top area, but it also provided access to the export route through Pwll-du tunnel, 545 yards (500m) to the north (pp. 52, 61).

Trams crossed to the top of the tower from the hillside by an embankment and a bridge. The current

Right: Despite the fine masonry at the front of the balance tower, no effort was made to hide the rubble stonework at the back.

Opposite: The balance tower built around 1839 to lift loaded wagons to the upper level of the works.

Above: Part of the timber trestle that once provided access to the balance tower from the hillside, exposed during excavations. The trestle was replaced by the masonry bridge that still stands.

Right: A reconstruction drawing of the balance tower in operation (Illustration by Peter Visscher, 2005).

Below: The parish register for 3 February 1840 records the burial of Thomas Waters, a labourer from Staffordshire, at the lift or 'guillotine'. The name guillotine may have been suggested by the sight of lifts dropping swiftly behind the arches (Gwent Record Office, D/Pa.74.17).

BURIALS in the Parish of _Lanover at Blaenafon_ in the County of _Monmouth_ in the Year 18**40**				
Name.	Abode.	When buried.	Age.	By whom the Ceremony was performed.
Peter Jenkins Son of Arthur Jenkins Labourer, & Margaret. No. 713.	*Brickyard*	*2. Febry*	*4 months*	*Jos. Jenkins*
Thomas Waters a Labourer, of Bilson Staffordshire, killed at lift. or guillotine. No. 714.	*Blaenafon*	*3 Febry*	*19.*	*J. Jenkins*

masonry bridge is cut into the tower, showing that it was a later addition (excavations have discovered fragments of an earlier timber trestle). Early in 1840 a 19-year-old labourer, Thomas Waters, died at the new lift. It would have been easy to stumble into the unguarded shaft while manhandling heavy wagons, or to fall from the bridge, which had no parapets. Breaking chains were another hazard. The impressive buttresses of the tower may have been added to halt subsidence during construction, but their uneven stone coursing bears witness that these too moved, even as they were being built. The lift fell out of use about 1880. Many ironworks had lifts, but that at Blaenavon is more complete than any in Britain. Water balances were also used at the well-drained local mines.

Operating the Balance Lift

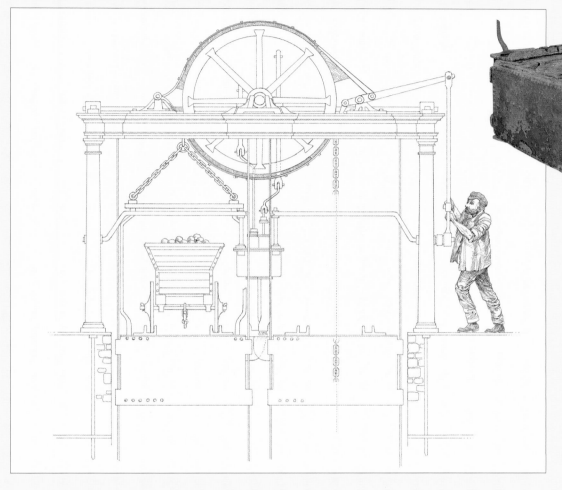

Above: The surviving lift car found in the base of the balance tower. Tram plates sit on top of the water tank, between the broken-off bars of the cradle from which it hung. Corroded guide wires still pass through shoes at each corner, and the locking pins extend from between the tram plates. The water scoop for filling the tank is on the far side.

Left: A reconstruction drawing of the balance gear showing the brake mechanism that clamped around the balance wheel (Illustration by John van Laun and Michael Blackmore).

The lift used the weight of water to raise a load — a form of 'renewable energy'. A chain, bearing a lift car at each end, passed over a grooved balance wheel, so that as one car went down the other was raised. Each car consisted of an iron water tank topped by tram plates onto which a wagon could be wheeled. The iron frame supported the wheel above the shaft. Its elegant columns are hollow cast iron, fixed by long bolts through stonework sandwiched by iron plates. The frame was mitred in a square, originally with four intermediate beams. The central two beams held the wheel, while slots in the outer pair suspended eight guide wires to keep the cars from swaying. Water came by a main that rises through the bridge.

A driver operated the braking and locking mechanisms and controlled the water flow. Labourers pushed wagons across the bridge to whichever car was at the top — fragments of tram plates show there were points to reach either side of the shaft. Wagons were then secured on the cars by dropping bars across the tram plates. The driver opened a valve letting up to 2.9 tons of water into the tank and pulled a lever to withdraw locking bolts. The cars moved slowly and silently at first, but speeded up as the weight of the chain transferred. A brake clamped to the wheel prevented the plunging tank from smashing to the bottom. As it landed on timber buffers a spike pushed up a plug to empty the water, while the upward car was swiftly locked at the top.

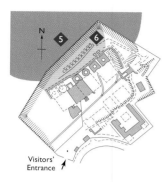

Dowlais Ironworks, Merthyr Tydfil, in 1840, by George Childs (active 1826–73). Men and women are shown shovelling coke near a plateway wagon. Flames pour from the tunnel heads atop the furnaces. By this time Dowlais was the greatest ironworks in the world, with eighteen furnaces, nine of which are visible here (National Museum of Wales).

A female wagon-oiler drawn at Blaenavon by A. J. Munby in 1865. Many women were employed in the upper yard in the processing of ore and the preparation of coke for the blast furnaces (A. J. Munby Collection, © Master and Fellows of Trinity College, Cambridge).

The Upper Yard ◆5

The top of the balance tower is a good place from which to look across the valley to Big Pit and to see the site of the upper yard, which extended for 220 yards (200m) behind the furnaces. Raw materials were brought by trams and packhorses and prepared by women and children or unskilled men. Coal was part-burned to make coke; limestone and iron ore were broken up; and 'cinders' were stockpiled to be remelted. In 1800, about 10–12 tons of materials were needed to make one ton of iron. The twelve-hour working day on these exposed hills must have seemed like a sentence to hard labour. The parish register for January 1822 recorded, 'Elizabeth Trew fell down on the ice with a bucket of coals on her head and died the same evening, aged 20'. It says much about the harshness of rural life that people poured into south Wales in search of such work.

Iron ore was left to weather, then broken by hand. A. J. Munby, who drew the workers here in 1865, noted that a man would break the larger lumps, then '…the girls smash them up. They use heavy hammers… lifting the hammer over their heads and bringing it down with manly skill and force. Fine strong girls they were… they break stones thus from 6.00am to 6.00pm every day, ceasing only for breakfast and dinner and earn six or seven shillings a week.' The women became the same colour as the ironstone.

Coal was partially burned to drive off impurities to leave coke. For the first sixty years at Blaenavon, coal was charred in heaps smothered with earth or small coal. This was difficult to control, especially in high winds, when vast quantities could be wasted. Workers were at risk from carbon monoxide poisoning and horrific burns. A nearby coke yard was described by William Needham in 1831 as a scene from hell: 'The long rows of flame produced by the burning of many hundred tons of coal, extending over a vast space of ground, and flickering in the wind, the black, grotesque figures of the cokers brandishing their long rakes, and partially visible through the thick lurid smoke, with the roaring of the blast and the noise of the machinery…'. Enclosed coke ovens, though invented in the seventeenth century, were not widespread until the mid-nineteenth. Banks of them were introduced at Blaenavon by the manager, Richard Johnson, in 1849 (p. 13). Open heaps were still used, but the new ovens were efficient, and more were built in 1875 and later.

The Furnace Tops

This narrow terrace was where materials were gathered to feed the insatiable furnaces. Everyone here worked twelve-hour shifts for seven days a week. Ironstone was roasted in the row of calcining kilns. Ore, limestone and coke were shovelled into two-wheeled barrows or 'dandies' and pushed over bridges to the furnaces. There were 'charging houses' on the bridges, until they were removed in the late nineteenth century to make access faster. The furnace tops were originally surrounded by 'tunnel heads', with doorways through which barrows were emptied into the flames. Combustible gases shot from the tops of the furnaces at 200 to 300 degrees Celsius. In about 1860, flues were built to take these gases to be utilized in the boilers, drawn by the great chimney in Stack Square.

Workers here took the night shift every other week, working for twenty-four hours when changing over. Timothy McCarthy (p. 22) was a 'filler' in 1841 and had his two sons helping him. Tim was probably aged 9 and Tom 7 (although McCarthy told a Government inspector they were 14 and 10). Tom had ruptured himself, but wore a home-made truss and his father said, 'the little chap does very well'. Both boys worked the same hours as their father, including night shifts.

The lumps of iron ore were roasted in the calcining kilns to remove sulphur, moisture and mud. One pair of kilns has been excavated, but there were fourteen here in 1880. Inside, a flat-sided cone of firebrick narrows to a grate. Ore and coke were thrown continuously into the top and roasted ore

Above: The surviving charging-house arch atop the furnace bank at Clydach Ironworks, to the north of Blaenavon and built just a few years later (Peter Wakelin).

Above left: The calcining kilns behind the furnaces where iron ore was roasted to remove impurities before smelting.

Below left: Large barrows, or 'dandies', for charging the furnaces through a tunnel head, at Lilleshall Ironworks, Shropshire, in 1951 (Black Country Living Museum, W. K. V. Gale Archive).

Below: Throat armouring at the top of Furnace 5. These iron strakes directed falling materials to prevent them from damaging the furnace lining or gathering against the sides.

A photograph of a Welsh 'pit girl' taken around 1860 by William Clayton of Tredegar (National Museum of Wales).

Children at Work

Children played an important part in the workforce at Blaenavon. Some worked from the age of 5, and most worked by their early teens, either for wages or to help their parents, who were paid according to the amount of work they completed. The Government commission on children's employment in 1842 found 185 children under the age of 13 working at Blaenavon Ironworks and its associated mines (almost a tenth of the workforce), and another 270 aged 13 to 18. A quarter were girls. The largest proportion worked at the ironstone patches, where iron ore was broken up, but some were employed at the furnaces and forges and many worked underground. Like their parents, children worked twelve-hour shifts, six or seven days a week. The investigators reported many individual cases:

• 'Margaret Thomas [age 15] has been working in the levels under ground pushing the trams in and out. Working in the levels was harder work than working on the mine-bank. The levels were mostly wet; sometimes she went through mud and water in them "half leg deep." She worked barefoot; there were many girls as young as her in the levels....They worked for the man that took the mine [ironstone], to fill by the ton; they sometimes got 10s. per week

and sometimes less; they would rather come to work than stay at home or go out to service.'

• 'Lucretia Jones, aged 8. Her work is to call out "haul up" to the man at the waterwheel when the signal is given in the pit that the trams are ready. She has not been there long; she waits in the lodge while the trams are coming up, and runs about; she is by the pit all day, but goes home to her dinner.'

• William Lloyd, the furnace manager, said, 'There are six boys in the cast-house and refinery from 10 to 14 years old. The refinery boys work in some heat in the summer time and sometimes get burned, but not very bad....I do not think that the children are put on to do more than they are able; I have not seen an instance of it here. I went to work when I was about eight years old to help the fillers at an iron-works in Staffordshire. I worked a good deal harder at it than the boys do here.'

Child labour was disliked, yet it was feared that controls would reduce prosperity and infringe personal freedoms. Legal restrictions were placed only on textile factories initially, but the Mines Act of 1842 forbade employment of children under 10 below ground.

An engraving of young children working underground in a British mine in the mid-nineteenth century. One child is pushing a dram of coal, while another is sitting in the darkness to open the ventilation door when needed. These were common jobs for children at Blaenavon in the early nineteenth century (Science Museum/Science & Society Picture Library).

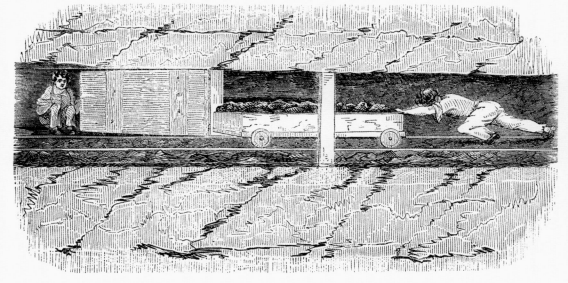

Far left: A cast-iron floor plate excavated in the charging area which is shaped to allow the barrows to be pushed back onto the plateway track. A cast-iron plateway sleeper is still attached at the far side.

Left: The remains of the brick flue that runs the whole length of the bank behind the furnaces. It is buried about 13 feet (4m) below the surface.

was raked out through the arch. Between the kilns a stockpile of limestone can still be seen. Iron plates on the floor made shovelling easier and allowed barrows to be rolled smoothly. They must have been laid after the charging houses had been cleared away since they cross the truncated walls. As a result, the whole charging area was raised by a few feet. The curved edge of some of the plates shows that they were reused from the lips of the furnaces. Another plate had flanges coming to a point to help move the barrows back onto tram plates. Foundations behind Furnace 5 incorporate a weighing house for measuring out the materials.

'Downcomer' flues were inserted behind each furnace in about 1860 to pull the waste gas into a brick tunnel that still runs the whole length of the bank about 13 feet (4m) below the surface. The tunnel is connected to the surface by brick shafts. These let off gas pressure and the force of any explosions, and also gave access to remove the build-up of dust. The gas was drawn through iron pipes across the yard, and into the boiler fires. Constructing the flue within the furnace bank must have been an enormous operation. Much of the retaining wall had to be taken down, and great arches were built to prevent the furnace bridges from pushing over the remaining sections as they were dug behind. Some of the furnaces later had the more efficient 'cup and cone' installed — a system of cantilevers which raised and lowered a conical lid. The cone served to distribute the raw materials evenly as they fell into the furnace and to deflect the gas into the downcomers.

Below left: Iron columns for carrying blast air pipes across the yard from the blowing engines to the furnaces, and return flues for waste furnace gas to be taken to the boilers. The bases of other such columns can be seen around the yard.

Below: A photograph of the ironworks probably taken in the first decade of the twentieth century. The scale of the pipes crossing the yard is evident; in the background one can be seen to have been truncated, suggesting that at least some of the furnaces were no longer in operation (Torfaen Museum Trust).

*The Development of
Blaenavon Ironworks*

About 1798
*As shown in Colt Hoare's
watercolour. The first three furnaces
have been set out, with the blowing
engine between them, and a coal
level opens into the yard. Stack
Square consists of key workers'
housing and a central range
containing the offices, manager's
house and company shop.*

About 1814
*The yard has been extended and
a second blowing-engine house
and two more furnaces have
been added. More housing has
been provided.*

About 1863 (illustrated far right)
*The ironworks at the height of its
development. The balance tower
has been built and the cast houses
refronted. Six furnaces range from
the earliest of the 1780s to the latest
circular type, built in 1861, where
the second engine house stood. A
foundry has replaced the first engine
house. Two newer engines have
boilers fed by waste gas drawn
across the yard by the chimney. The
shop has been converted to cottages.*

About 1900
*Most new development has been
across the valley at the Forgeside
works. Two early furnaces have
been replaced with a much larger
circular one. Hot-blast stoves have
been installed.*

*Far right: A reconstruction
drawing of Blaenavon Ironworks
in around 1863 (Illustration by
Michael Blackmore 2002).*

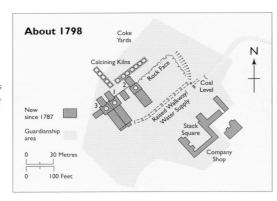

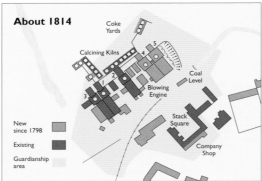

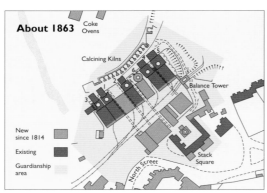

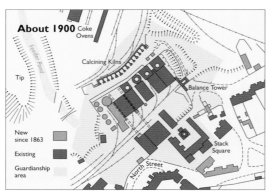

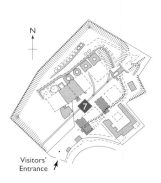

Visitors' Entrance

Above: A drawing of the façades of the foundry and Furnace 2 cast house (pp. 44–45). The foundry (left) was probably built by James Ashwell in around the late 1830s. The large arch must have been inserted in 1860, when the huge flywheel for the new engine was cast here. The cast houses were probably refronted by Ashwell. The openings let out heat and fumes (Illustration by Neil Daniels).

Right: The massive foundations of the 1860 engine house, with the deep flywheel pit at the centre.

Right: Few beam blowing engines survive in Britain. David & Sampson, built by Murdock Aitken and Company of Glasgow in 1851 for Priorslee Ironworks in Shropshire, are now preserved at the Ironbridge Gorge Museum (Ironbridge Gorge Museum).

The Blowing Engines

The massive foundations at the bottom of the track from the upper yard mark the site of the 1860 engine house. It was built to house the last in the succession of four steam blowing engines — built in 1789, 1800, 1819 and 1860 — which blew blast air to the furnaces, acting like giant bellows for a fire. Half of the length of the 1860 building is visible, including the deep pit for the flywheel. Two horizontal steam cylinders were held down by the massive bolts. The 25-ton central flywheel, 23 feet (7m) in diameter, was cast in the foundry opposite, where the archway specially made in the façade is just 6 inches (150mm) wider.

The 1789 engine house lay between Furnaces 1 and 2, and the 1800 engine house on the site later occupied by Furnace 6. The 1819 engine house lay under the viewing platform to the north. Two iron columns across the yard carried the blast pipes to the furnaces or gas flues back. The 1819 and 1860 engines, which continued to operate alongside one another, were served by fourteen steam boilers. Two coal levels opened directly into the yard to supply fuel, and the seam they mined became known as 'the engine coal'. What was probably the original water supply to feed the boilers, near the balance tower, was replaced by a watercourse of just over a mile (2km) in length in 1801 (the 'feeder to the steam engines' on Deakin's map of 1819, p. 10). Even this was not enough in the drought of 1868, when a pump was brought in to recirculate supplies.

Steam Power for Blowing

Steam power was one of the crucial inventions of the Industrial Revolution, freeing many industries from the tyranny of water power. Ironworks could not operate without sufficient power, since a furnace could be ruined if the blast was interrupted. Before steam, ironworks needed to be located close to reliable water supplies; they were limited in size and had to stop work during droughts.

The first practical engines, of the 'atmospheric' type invented by Thomas Newcomen in 1712, could aid blowing by pumping back water to keep waterwheels supplied, a technique first used at Coalbrookdale in 1743 and applied at ten ironworks or more in Shropshire during the next thirty years. The first direct blowing engine was installed at John Wilkinson's Willey Ironworks in Shropshire in 1776. Wilkinson devised a water balance to regulate the air pressure from an engine made by Boulton & Watt. Direct blowing was quickly taken up at several existing works and at Wilkinson's new works at Snedshill, Shropshire, in 1777–79. Blaenavon was probably only the second ironworks in the world to be devised around steam power. Its succession of blowing engines illustrates the remarkable speed of change in the iron industry in output, engine design and furnace practice.

1789 The lack of water power at the site and Colt Hoare's early depiction both indicate that steam power was used from the beginning. The maker of the original engine at Blaenavon has not been discovered, but it was one of the first dozen blowing engines in the world. Colt Hoare showed two chimneys through the roof from internal boilers. It may have been an atmospheric engine, or a steam engine by Wilkinson or another of the manufacturers considered 'pirates' of Boulton & Watt's patents. The site lay to the left of Furnace 2, partially beneath what is now the foundry. There may be opportunities to excavate this in future.

1800 The first engine was joined by a Boulton & Watt beam engine, situated where the remains of Furnace 6 now stand. This would have provided more blast for the new furnaces, and a fallback should the old engine fail. Design drawings show a 40-inch (1m) cylinder driving a rocking beam 26 feet (7.9m) long. It was demolished to build Furnace 6 in 1860.

1819 This beam engine was only the second ever made by the Neath Abbey Iron Company, based near Swansea, which became one of the best-known steam engineering companies in the world. A cylinder of 52.5 inches (1.3m) diameter drove a beam with one stroke every five seconds. With a diameter of 104 inches (2.6m), the blowing cylinder produced 11,184 cubic feet of air a minute. The handsome engine house was four storeys high with a hipped roof. The arrival of this third engine allowed the first to be taken out of service.

1860 The company reading room was demolished to make way for what was to be the last engine house. The minutes recorded, 'the Old Blowing engine which from incessant work since the last century has become almost in a dangerous state, has been replaced by a new one'. The two steam cylinders, each 90 inches (2.3m) in diameter, were capable of blowing 14,380 cubic feet per minute to three of the furnaces. Although designed by Boulton & Watt, parts were made at Blaenavon. The central flywheel pit and steam cylinder bases have been exposed.

The surviving blowing-engine house at Ynysfach, Merthyr Tydfil, of similar style to the 1819 engine house at Blaenavon (HERIAN).

An original design drawing by Boulton & Watt showing a section through the second blowing engine at Blaenavon, built in 1800. The rocking beam connects the steam cylinder (right) to the blowing cylinder (left). Outside the engine house (far right) is a boiler (Birmingham City Archives, Ms. 3147/5/673).

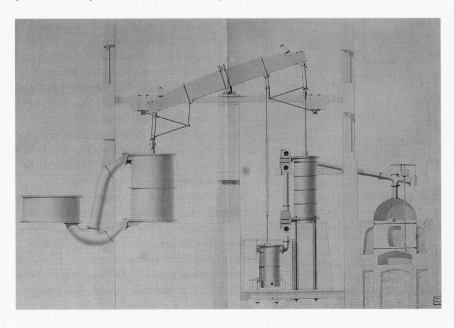

Above: Plateway tracks and points at the base of the balance tower. A double gauge allowed both trams and furnace barrows to be carried on the lift.

Above right: The removal of the outer masonry of Furnaces 4 and 5 in 1911 to build St James's Church created great conservation problems, but allows the internal construction to be seen (John Lewis).

The Base of the Balance Tower ⬥8

The balance lift (pp. 26–29) was connected to a network of tramroads said in 1837 to amount to over 35 miles (56km). A set of L-shaped tramroad plates, intact with junction points, survives within the archway at the front of the tower. The ingenious dual-gauge track at the lift was able to carry tramroad wagons of 2-feet (610mm) gauge and barrows of 3-feet (910mm) gauge. At the bottom of the shaft the lift cars came to rest on timber baulks and the water flowed down a drain. A surviving car, complete with water tank, was found here (p. 29).

The standard-gauge track on wooden sleepers in front of the tower was installed after 1854 as a network of locomotive railways around Blaenavon made it easier to move materials. Wagons of red-hot slag were carried to tips in the valley and pig iron could be taken in bulk to the Forgeside works and onto the national rail network. The level of the yard was raised, and the rails are 18 inches (0.5m) higher than the old plateway tracks.

The left corner of the tower was once inside the cast house that served Furnace 5, and the scar left where the wall joined the balance tower is visible to the right of the niche. A coal adit — a mining tunnel — once entered the hillside here.

Furnaces 4 and 5 ⬥9

The blast furnaces were where the roasted iron ore was smelted with coke and limestone (pp. 5–6). Furnaces 4 and 5 were added during the second decade of the ironworks' operation. Their outer masonry casing has been robbed, partly revealing the firebrick interior, which was cut out for relining every few years. (Blaenavon had its own yards to produce the millions of heat-resistant bricks.) At Furnace 4 the dam plate and tap hole survive (blocked with iron from the last charge), where the furnaceman used a bar to break open a clay bung: with spurts of liquid metal, this was a hazardous place to work. The iron was run into sand beds to form pigs — so called because the casting channels resembled sows with piglets suckling. Slag was tapped periodically and taken away by wagons in the low-level bay.

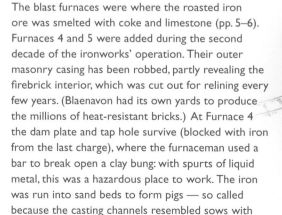

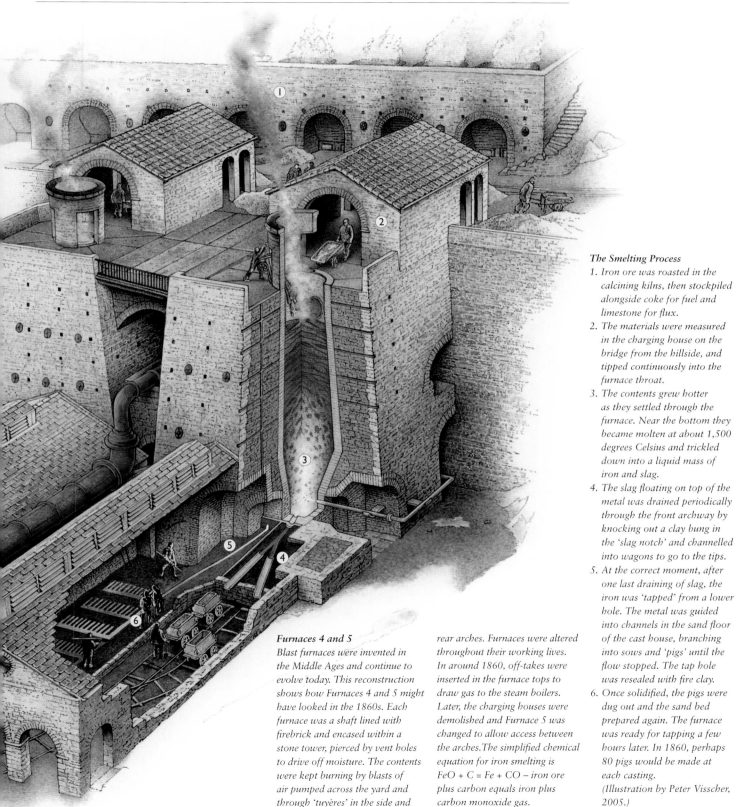

The Smelting Process

1. Iron ore was roasted in the calcining kilns, then stockpiled alongside coke for fuel and limestone for flux.
2. The materials were measured in the charging house on the bridge from the hillside, and tipped continuously into the furnace throat.
3. The contents grew hotter as they settled through the furnace. Near the bottom they became molten at about 1,500 degrees Celsius and trickled down into a liquid mass of iron and slag.
4. The slag floating on top of the metal was drained periodically through the front archway by knocking out a clay bung in the 'slag notch' and channelled into wagons to go to the tips.
5. At the correct moment, after one last draining of slag, the iron was 'tapped' from a lower hole. The metal was guided into channels in the sand floor of the cast house, branching into sows and 'pigs' until the flow stopped. The tap hole was resealed with fire clay.
6. Once solidified, the pigs were dug out and the sand bed prepared again. The furnace was ready for tapping a few hours later. In 1860, perhaps 80 pigs would be made at each casting.

(Illustration by Peter Visscher, 2005.)

Furnaces 4 and 5

Blast furnaces were invented in the Middle Ages and continue to evolve today. This reconstruction shows how Furnaces 4 and 5 might have looked in the 1860s. Each furnace was a shaft lined with firebrick and encased within a stone tower, pierced by vent holes to drive off moisture. The contents were kept burning by blasts of air pumped across the yard and through 'tuyères' in the side and rear arches. Furnaces were altered throughout their working lives. In around 1860, off-takes were inserted in the furnace tops to draw gas to the steam boilers. Later, the charging houses were demolished and Furnace 5 was changed to allow access between the arches. The simplified chemical equation for iron smelting is $FeO + C = Fe + CO$ – iron ore plus carbon equals iron plus carbon monoxide gas.

Right: A photograph of the ironworks yard during its working life, probably taken in the 1890s. The balance tower dominates the right of the picture, its balance wheel still in place. The corner of the 1819 engine house is just to the right, and two of the great blast mains cross the yard on iron columns. On the far left are the Cowper hot-blast stoves, probably installed in the 1880s, and in front of them a building which appears to have been a pair of cottages. The large new furnace, which replaced Furnaces 1 and 3, is hidden (the cast house for Furnace 3 is in ruins), but the others are all visible in a row: Furnace 2, with a crane for a cup and cone operation; the circular Furnace 6; and the square tops of Furnaces 4 and 5 beyond. The standard-gauge rail wagons in the foreground are all loaded with pigs. Curious staff are looking out at the photographer from the door to the workshop (National Museum of Wales).

Below: The tapping area of Furnace 4, showing the great hearthstone at the bottom and above it the iron dam plate and tap hole. Behind this the firebrick lining has been broken through into the furnace.

Furnace keepers maximized production by exercising careful judgement about the mix of materials, the force of blast and the times of tapping. Productivity grew from an average of 35 tons a week from each furnace in 1796 to 50 tons in 1805 and well over 100 tons in 1843. Furnace 4 (built 1801) and Furnace 5 to its right (1807) were typical large furnaces of the period, 48-feet (15m) high. Furnaces were blown-out every few years to be relined and sometimes alterations were made. Ashwell rebuilt one furnace around 1840: perhaps Furnace 5, which has distinctive buttresses to the hillside. In about the 1880s Furnace 5 was altered to run a circular blast main around the furnace bowl and hot blast (p. 43) may have been introduced, as an iron tuyère pipe found here (through which the blast was blown into the furnace) was water cooled to prevent it melting.

Looking into the front of Furnace 4, the huge hearthstone is at the bottom. The quality of hearthstones was vital, and in 1788 they were brought from the Midlands before local sources were identified. This one has split, and molten iron has rushed down the cracks. Its position so far forward suggests that the previous dam failed and that the forehearth was hastily rebuilt. The platform for the cast houses can still be made out. In the slag bay, the railway is unusually constructed of cast iron and may have carried plateway barrows as well as standard-gauge wagons. Beyond this is the pivot plate for a crane to swing pigs onto wagons from the cast house. A small engine to power it probably stood on the brick floor, where a photograph of the 1890s (above) caught a puff of steam.

Left: The site today from the same viewpoint as that of the 1890s photograph.

Left: A blast furnace of about the 1840s at Dowlais Ironworks, Merthyr Tydfil, which is similar to Furnace 6 in having upper parts of firebrick in iron bands (though it has a square rather than a circular base). The economy of construction and relining are obvious by comparison with the older furnace beyond. The photograph, dated about 1870, also shows blast and gas pipes, open pig beds, waiting slag trams, and pigs levered up ready for collection (Glamorgan Archives).

Furnace 6 ◆10

The fragmentary remains of Furnace 6 illustrate the evolution of blast furnaces from the masonry towers used since the late Middle Ages to the metal-clad furnaces of today. Furnace 6, 'blown-in' on 11 April 1861, dispensed with a full stone casing in favour of a circular base with a firebrick tower bound by iron straps. This type was cheaper to construct and easy to dismantle when relining was needed. It was said to work 'in a capital manner'. Even though only the base survives, it is the most complete example in Britain.

Blaenavon's second engine house and the boilers for the Boulton & Watt engine of 1800 stood on this spot, but were demolished to make way for Furnace 6 and its cast house. The retaining wall behind the furnaces, from which some bedrock still outcrops, was probably built about the same time as the engine. The upper third of the wall was dismantled and rebuilt in about 1860 to insert the flue that ran the whole length of the bank to carry waste furnace gas (p. 33). A blocked exit to one of the pipes that crossed the yard from the flue can be made out to the right of Furnace 6.

The cast house, of which the platform survives, may have been iron framed. The iron objects in front of the cast house are ingot moulds made here and used across the valley at Forgeside steelworks. Molten steel was poured into them from Bessemer converters. When it had solidified the mould was lifted off to leave the ingot. The moulds had a life of perhaps seventy casts. Although used in their millions after the 1850s, examples are rare.

Below: The surviving base of Furnace 6, the most complete example of this type of furnace to survive in Britain.

*Right: The interior of Furnace 2,
one of the earliest furnaces at
the site. The base of the furnace
was cut out in preparation for
a relining, probably in around
1900 when production was
coming to an end, and the work
was not completed.*

*The side of Furnace 2 (right)
and the tall retaining wall below
the charging bank. The circular
opening near the top of the wall
is where the flue carrying the
waste gas from the furnaces
crossed the yard.*

Furnace 2

Furnace 2 is one of the earliest at the ironworks
and appears on the right of Colt Hoare's drawing
(pp. 4, 20–21). The interior has been cut out at the
base, ready for a relining that never took place,
allowing a view up through the furnace. The firebrick
is cracked and smothered with iron — blast furnaces
worked continuously for years until relining was
essential. The area around head height was where
the iron became molten, at about 1,500 degrees
Celsius: hotter than volcanic lava flows. The back
and side arches were for blowing, and a section of
blast main lies in the rear passage.

The interior shape is like an inverted wine bottle.
The missing section would have been the bottle's neck.
The diameter is wider than Furnaces 4 or 5, and it was
remodelled, possibly in 1877, with the insertion of a
circular blast route around the shaft to connect the
arches (as at Furnace 5). A ring beam, fitted by Cadw,
prevents the lining from collapsing. The alcove in the
cliff behind helped when manoeuvring the blowing
pipes and tuyères. The passage separated the furnace
from the hillside to prevent water from reaching the
molten iron, as this could create an explosion. Such a
burst reportedly injured several men at Blaenavon in 1870.

The Sites of Other Furnaces

The scale of the retaining wall and Furnace 2 is
best appreciated from the viewing area outside
the side arch. The iron tie plates restrained the
furnace as it expanded with the heat, and the
weep holes made sure that moisture was driven
off safely. Cast-iron brackets supported blast mains.
The retaining wall was faced in firebricks in the
late nineteenth century, but rock still protrudes.
The circular opening high up connected to the gas
flue behind. The first blowing engine stood on this
spot, with the other two early furnaces (Furnaces
1 and 3) beyond. These were replaced by a far
larger furnace in around 1878. A row of hot-blast
stoves was added later.

The 1870s furnace could produce 200 tons of iron
a week, almost double the older furnaces at their best,
and was the next stage in furnace evolution. A few
courses of firebricks protrude above ground, and the
base may be excavated in the future. It was wider and
probably taller than its predecessors and appears to
have been entirely of firebrick, clad with plating. Similar
furnaces existed at Forgeside (p.13).

Beyond the 1870s furnace stood four hot-blast stoves: one can be seen at the far left in a photograph of the 1890s (pp. 40–41). Preheating of blast air was invented by James Neilson (1792–1865) in 1828. This typically resulted in a fuel saving of twenty per cent, and more as techniques improved. At Blaenavon, it was tried within five years of its invention, but it was not pursued, probably because of the cheapness and quality of local coal. It also affected the iron, and cold-blast pig remained a sought-after material, which the old works continued to make throughout its life. Nevertheless, hot blast was reintroduced at some of the furnaces after 1880. The stove in the photograph was of the Cowper type. Devised in 1860, this was a metal-clad tower packed with star-shaped bricks made red-hot by burning gas from the furnaces. The four stoves worked alternately so that the blast air was warmed by flowing through one, while the others were being heated. A chimney — the base of which is on top of the retaining wall — provided the draught. The collection of waste gas to heat the stoves was assisted by the cup and cone system of closing the furnace tops (p. 33). A crane for this can be seen on Furnace 2 in the 1890s photograph.

The Cast House

The cast house glowed with intense heat and red light when the molten iron flowed into the pig beds — the openings in the walls provided ventilation. The floor area gives some idea of the amount of iron produced. In the 1860s perhaps eighty to a hundred pigs were made at each twelve-hourly tapping. Six cast houses protected the sand beds at this works alone. Few others survive in Britain as many were dispensed with to aid bulk production, but at Blaenavon they were retained until the works closed. Among iron objects here are a 'sow' left from a branching runnel of iron and a few of the pigs that were the prime product of the works. The name BLAENAVON can be made out on some — a pig and a stamp for forming the mark in the sand are in the visitor centre.

Judging by Colt Hoare's watercolour, the side wall remains much as it was built in about 1788, but the front was remodelled, probably during James Ashwell's reorganization in the late 1830s. The roof appears to have been made of clay pantiles originally, but the present wrought-iron trusses, which date from the late nineteenth century, would have been covered, as now, with corrugated-iron sheets. Some of the fine casting sand remains on the floor, though now much mixed with ash.

Most pig iron was converted at forges into wrought iron, the malleable material for rails, tools, chains, plates and thousands of other products. Although small forges existed in the yard, most wrought iron was made in satellite works such as Garnddyrys (pp. 54–56). The company made all its own tools, many examples of which are around the cast house. The elegant wrought-iron tollgate comes from the Blaenavon turnpike road, and probably dates from the 1830s. More examples of cast-iron work can be seen at St Peter's Church (p. 49). The fireclay crucibles date from the early twentieth century, when the old ironworks was a maintenance yard with a brass foundry in this building.

A star-shaped refractory brick used for heat exchange in the Cowper stoves in the 1890s.

Above: A detail of a watercolour of around 1810 by Thomas Tudor (1785–1855) showing molten iron being run out into pig beds (National Library of Wales).

Left: Furnace 2 with its cast house, and the foundry to its left. The fragmentary base of the chimney that served the Cowper stoves is on the horizon above the foundry.

Some Examples of Iron Products

Right: A Blaenavon pig of cast iron, the basic product of the works. Each pig was marked with the company name, by impressing a stamp in the sand beds, to act as an advertisement and to control the stock.

Above: A cast-iron tramroad wheel of plateway type.

Cast iron is produced direct from the blast furnace, or remelted to make cast objects at foundries. The material is brittle, but strong in compression.

- Pigs — the basic material from the furnaces, remelted to make other cast objects, or processed to make wrought iron or steel
- Tie plates — flat plates cast in sand beds
- Beams and columns — strong structural elements that revolutionized building technology
- Tram wheels — usually cast in one piece, but sometimes composites of wrought and cast elements
- Tram plates — short L-shaped plates for tram wheels to run on
- Casting boxes — boxes to contain foundry sand in two-part moulds for complex castings
- Window frames — examples can be seen at Engine Row and St Peter's Church

Wrought iron is produced by reprocessing pig iron in puddling forges. It can then be rolled or smithed. The material is easily worked and strong in tension.

- Bar iron — the basic material, sent to smiths' shops to work into other objects
- Rails — the most important product of the Welsh iron industry, manufactured in rolling mills and used to build railways all over the world
- Chains — forged from bar iron
- Tie bars — made in the rolling mills
- Hand tools — individually made in smiths' forges
- Angle iron sections — used in many structures, including roof trusses
- Plate iron — riveted to make tanks, boilers, cladding and iron ships
- Corrugated iron — a new building material from the mid-nineteenth century

N

Visitors'
Entrance ↑

The surviving cupola furnace standing at the front of the foundry, used to remelt iron for smaller castings. It is a structure of firebrick within wrought-iron plates. The blast ports are visible, and it was tapped through the doorway into the foundry.

The Foundry ◆14

This well-organized foundry for making cast objects appears to have been built during Ashwell's redevelopment in the late 1830s. Iron could be cast direct from Furnaces 1 and 2 through the side arches near the back, or remelted in small 'cupola' furnaces like that outside the front wall. The foundry was part of the company's maintenance depot long after smelting stopped at the old works in 1900.

Cupolas were shaft furnaces for remelting iron, patented by John Wilkinson in 1794. This one probably dates from the late nineteenth century. It is made of firebricks covered with riveted wrought-iron plates. The blast ports and the tap hole can be seen. The furnace would have been lit when needed. It was charged using a hoist, but there are also remains of steps up to it from behind. A small reverberatory furnace, also for remelting iron, may have stood on the opposite side of the main archway. In reverberatory furnaces the fuel was kept separate from the metal, which was heated by flame bouncing off a brick vault.

The whole floor of the building was used for casting. Vessels of molten iron were passed around on cranes, brackets for which can be seen over the front arch and on the side wall. Castings were created by first making a wooden pattern of the object to be cast, scaled up to allow for shrinkage. For a casting with one flat side, the pattern could be just pressed into the sand floor, then carefully removed to leave its shape. More complex forms were made in moulding boxes: frames in two or more parts that were filled with fine sand bound with oil to take the shape of a pattern, then bolted together. Molten iron was poured in through a hole. If the object was to be hollow, a core was placed inside, pinned to leave a gap around it. An inventory at Christmas 1850 recorded 111 tons of mould boxes and cores.

Behind the foundry are the walls and front beam of a stove for drying moulds. This had a vaulted roof held tight by iron bars between the posts on either side. A flue drew hot air through. A second stove lay behind the arch to the right and must have been built after Furnace 2 went of use. The stoves indicate how busy the foundry was, making cast objects to use all over the works.

The Pay Office and the Gilchrist Thomas Memorial

As you leave the site, the full scale of the furnace bank is visible, including an area on the left that has partly fallen away and exposed a section of the gas flue. The chimney in the yard (about half its original height) probably served the core stoves and remelting furnaces in the foundry, and the brick building next to it was a workshop. The office — now the visitor reception — was built in about 1850.

Workers passed through the corridor between the pair of doors, collecting their pay from the small windows. Beyond is a weighbridge house of about 1900, which was altered in the 1930s for coal lorries; the scales were in the building and the plate sat within the iron rim. Close by is a memorial to Sidney Gilchrist Thomas (p. 15). The level ground here and across the valley to Big Pit is made up of slag from more than a century of iron smelting, completely filling the original valley of the Afon Lwyd.

Above: A wall bracket for a timber crane to move vessels of molten iron around the foundry.

Top left: The remains of the stove, behind the rear of the foundry, for drying moulds. The iron posts supported tie bars for a vaulted brick roof.

The pay office, with doors at each end for queuing staff to collect wages. The roof originally extended as a canopy.

In the car park, the steam hammer was made by B&S Massey Ltd of Manchester around 1912. Steam hammers were invented by James Nasmyth in 1839 for use in forges. The steam cylinder at the top raised the hammer (which weighed 7 tons) then dropped it onto the anvil while metal was manoeuvred underneath. This example was brought to Daniel Doncaster & Sons' Forgeside works in the 1960s from Sheffield. One of its last jobs was to make parts for Concorde, the world's first supersonic airliner.

A Tour of the Blaenavon Industrial Landscape

The Blaenavon Industrial Landscape is a microcosm of the Industrial Revolution. This tour suggests seven key locations around the World Heritage Site that you may care to visit: some are viewpoints, others involve short walks. But there are many other features of interest that are well worth visiting and these are shown on the map inside the back cover.

The entire landscape was affected powerfully by the development of Blaenavon Ironworks. In some ways the landscape *was* the ironworks, for there were no real boundaries around the furnaces and the tentacles of the iron-making operation spread out across the whole of the surrounding hills. The partners owned or controlled almost all of the land around the works, and even the areas they did not control were transformed by the iron-making revolution.

An Evolving Townscape: Blaenavon

> From the ironworks car park, turn right at the bottom of the steps and right again to follow the curving main road downhill.

Blaenavon began as a cluster of houses and other buildings built by the iron company, near the ironworks and alongside the tramroad down the valley. Only a generation later did a town centre grow up, sited on a few parcels of land just off the coal measures that were not controlled by the company. Features typical of the prosperous iron-making towns of the south Wales valleys can be seen — shops and public houses, churches and chapels, the works' school, and a working men's institute, all surrounded by terraces of houses.

Opposite the road junction, the altered complex of buildings [1] was once the company shop, built in the 1840s when it was moved from Stack Square. This contained rooms for all the goods the community needed (p. 26) and a public house, officially called the Crown but known locally as the Drum and Monkey. Church Road [2], now the main road through Blaenavon, began life in 1793 as a horse-drawn 'railroad' to the Monmouthshire Canal

Opposite: The Blaenavon Industrial Landscape, looking from Pwll-du limestone quarry, beside the snaking line of Hill's tramroad, across Pen-ffordd-goch and Keeper's Pond towards Blaenavon. The extent of the coal measures is marked by the dark heather giving way to grass and bracken on the limestone soils (RCAHMW).

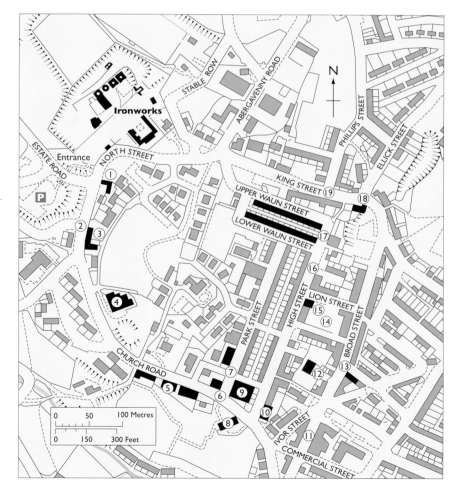

Blaenavon town from the air. The ironworks is just visible in the top right-hand corner. The line of the tramroad down the valley is now followed by the road, which curves around to the left past St Peter's School and Church. The ironmasters' mansion can be made out in its private woods. Broad Street, crossing the bottom of the picture from left to right, was laid out in the 1840s and colonized by shops, pubs and chapels to create a town centre in Blaenavon for the first time. Within a few decades, terraced housing extended all around this centre (RCAHMW).

Staffordshire Row and North Street was an unusual four-storey development of company housing built in the 1820s just below the ironworks. The upper two storeys, known as Staffordshire Row, were entered from the uphill side, while the lower two were built into the bank and opened to North Street. Shepherd Square adjoined them at the bottom. They were considered unsatisfactory in a Medical Report of 1909, but were not demolished until the 1960s.

St Peter's School with its Gothic-style windows and Latin dedication tablet is one of the prettiest buildings in the town and the oldest surviving works' school in Wales (Torfaen Museum Trust).

at Pontypool. It was graded so that wagons could roll down unaided and be hauled back by horses. Primitive railways like this set the framework for many iron-working settlements. Workers' houses clustered all around it until the 1960s: one row survives, abutting the road just down the hill [3].

Continuing down Church Road, the imposing residence of the managing partner of the ironworks is visible behind the wall on the left [4]. This was Great House (now The Beeches), built between 1798 and 1800 by Samuel Hopkins (p. 11). Its wooded grounds were enclosed by a wall capped with iron slag. For 150 years it looked onto fields set aside from mining to preserve the prospect of the whitewashed company farm across the valley.

To the right of the road beyond are the three buildings of St Peter's School [5], built in 1816, 1849 and 1860. That to the left, closest to the church and now the World Heritage Centre, is the earliest. Before this Samuel Hopkins and his sister, Sarah (1768–1844), had supported a few teachers, but education was still expensive for families, as they had to pay a contribution and also forego the wages which the children could have earned. After Samuel's untimely death, Sarah endowed St Peter's Free

School in his memory, where children could learn elementary reading, writing and arithmetic. When it opened in 1816, 120 students enrolled, but this was still far fewer than the number who continued to work. The local historian, Lewis Browning, recalled that while he went to school there in the 1830s, two of his younger brothers toiled underground to support the family. St Peter's is the oldest surviving works' school in Wales. The schoolroom was in the middle, with a master's cottage at one end and a schoolmistress's at the other. Across the road, the police station [6] was built in 1894. Behind this, Park Street Methodist Church of 1885 is visible [7].

St Peter's Church [8], among the trees beyond the school, was built by the ironmasters for their growing community in 1804 and consecrated in 1805. It was a simple example of the Gothic revival style before it became the norm for Anglican churches. Iron is to be seen everywhere, including the unique cast-iron font. The windows were iron, and when a gallery was inserted to accommodate the expanding congregation, it was supported by elegant iron columns. Among the monuments inside are memorials for Samuel Elmes Steele, the company surgeon, and the ironmasters Thomas Hill II,

Samuel Hopkins and Howard Kennard (1889–1903). In the churchyard are several tombs with cast-iron tops, including those for Hill and Thomas Deakin, who drew a plan of the Blaenavon area in 1819 (p. 10). The churchyard gateposts were cast from the same patterns as the columns of the balance tower at the ironworks.

The elaborately designed workmen's institute opposite [9], opened in 1895, was a vital focus of community life and self-education for the town (p. 16). The adjacent clock tower commemorates some of the Blaenavon men killed in the First World War.

The hillside behind was colonized by chapels, shops and houses from the 1840s to the 1860s as new streets were laid out. By 1901 there were eighteen places of worship. Horeb Baptist Chapel [10], opposite the churchyard, was established on another site by 1807, but was relocated here in 1862–63.

Continue down Church Road, turning left into Commercial Street and left again into Broad Street [11], the long shopping street that developed from the 1840s to form the heart of the town. It curves up a shallow cleft in the hillside, following the line of a stream culverted beneath (it was originally called Heol y Nant or 'Stream Street'). By the 1860s the

The extraordinary cast-iron font at St Peter's Church.

St Peter's Church, built by the ironmasters in 1804–05, who appointed a Welsh-speaking curate, James Jenkins of Llandeilo. The windows were of cast iron (RCAHMW).

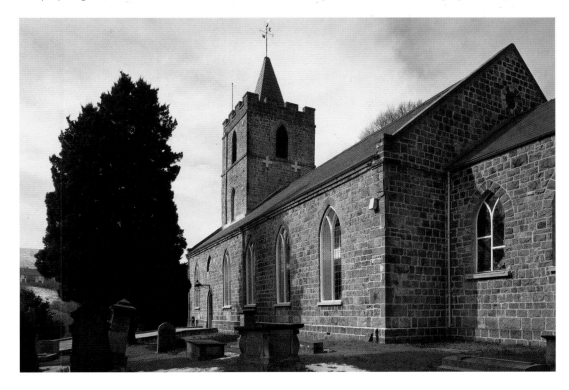

Above: A Blaenavon shop in King Street in the late nineteenth century (Mrs Mary Challenger).

Right: Blaenavon's Broad Street today. The street followed the curving line of a stream, now culverted beneath it. Chapels, shops and public houses colonized it from the 1840s.

The English Baptist Chapel, Moriah, on Broad Street, rebuilt in 1888 (RCAHMW).

street was filled with shops, mostly gas lit and open into the evenings, selling meat, groceries, clothes, boots, jewellery, glasswares and a vast range of other goods. By the 1990s over half the shops were derelict, but many have now come back into use.

In 1863, Blaenavon had forty-one pubs or beer-houses, many on Broad Street, such as the Castle, the Market Tavern and the Rolling Mill. Continue uphill to find Bethlehem Independent Chapel [12], set back in Bethlehem Square with its graveyard around it. The chapel was placed beside the stream in 1840, shortly before the street was set out. Almost opposite is the huge English Baptist Chapel [13] opened in 1847 and rebuilt in 1888 to serve the increasing numbers of English-speaking workers.

A left turn off Broad Street into Lion Street leads past Lion Square [14], once used for public meetings. It is easy to see from here how Broad Street sits within a gully in the hillside. At the top corner of the square are the former municipal offices, largely dating from the 1930s. These now house the Blaenavon library and a community heritage museum with a display about the novelist Alexander Cordell [15]. Beyond is High Street [16], laid out by speculative builders in the 1860s with narrow, two-up, two-down houses typical of south Wales industrial towns.

Turn right up the hill. The two terraces to the left, Upper and Lower Waun Street [17], were among the few in the town centre built by the Blaenavon Iron Company — fifty houses laid out in the Waun field in 1864–66. At the top of High Street, continue through the alley (Bethel Lane), past Bethel Baptist Church, opened in 1887 [18].

The curving lane across the hillside, which is now called King Street [19], was in existence by the sixteenth century and became one of the first places where people built houses independently of the ironmasters (some shown on Deakin's map of 1819, p.10). A Roman Catholic chapel was built near here in 1868, mainly to serve Irish workers. If you turn right, you can return to the top of Broad Street; or if you turn left you can return to the ironworks on North Street and the car park a short distance down hill.

Mining the Outcrops: Pen-ffordd-goch

Just after the summit of the B4246 Abergavenny road from Blaenavon there is a large car park to the right, beside a reservoir. Shown on maps as Pen-ffordd-goch Pond or Forge Pond, it is known locally as Keeper's Pond.

Keeper's Pond marks the very corner of the south Wales coalfield. Ground rich in coal and iron ore extends to the south and west, but to the north there is a limestone escarpment that falls away to the Usk valley. This summit is one of the best places to examine primitive patch workings for scouring out the ore. The reservoir supplied water power to Garnddyrys forge, a mile (1.6km) to the north. The hilltop is urban common, allowing free access on foot, but fenced areas are private. There are interesting walks in all directions, with views to the Brecon Beacons.

The coal measures come to an end in a triangle of land pointing towards the aerials, marked by the tips covered in heather, giving way to grass and bracken on the smooth slopes of the Blorenge. Before Blaenavon Ironworks was established, iron ore nodules were dug for furnaces at Pontypool, and bloomeries may have been used to make iron here in the Roman period or earlier. Miners built small ponds and watercourses along the contours and released water to scour away the surface soil or separate iron nodules from the lighter coal and shale. A map of 1812 shows scours that can still be picked out today, and the area has many low banks as a result of the construction of temporary reservoirs. The ironmasters sub-let the ground in 'patches' to individuals who worked with other miners or their families and sold back the ore they produced. Adit mines were driven into the hill for coal and iron ore, and the 1812 map names some of their lessees — David Davis, Edward Edwards and Morgan Edwards. The entrances have collapsed, but the V-shaped approaches and crow's-foot tips emerging from them can be seen.

Keeper's Pond held water for Garnddyrys forge, which was in operation by 1817–18 (pp. 9, 54–56), and it was probably built soon afterwards. Scouring must have stopped after the reservoir was built or it would have silted up immediately. Like industrial ponds throughout the heads of the valleys area, it was formed by an irregular stone-and-earth dam along the hillside, threaded through the tips. A network of watercourses led in and out of it: an overflow at the far end led down to Garnddyrys, and there is an outlet valve through the dam, some 20 feet (6m) below the water level.

The limestone that Blaenavon Ironworks needed as a flux in the furnaces had to be brought over this hilltop until the construction of Pwll-du tunnel. Across the dam, an almost level path continues for some 2 miles (3km) along the north-western slopes of the Blorenge, marking the line of a road or plateway, built about 1795, to a short-lived quarry. Low stone embankments survive along its route, but it was disused soon after 1800. A railroad, perhaps built in about 1789, came from Tyla quarries (p. 52) and crossed the ridge towards Blaenavon close to the present road. It has been argued that this may have been the first railway in the world to have all-iron rails.

The mining remains extend across the hilltop towards Blaenavon. The tree just beyond the summit marks the position of Pen-ffordd-goch machine, a weighbridge to check the quantities of limestone. Further on, at the first bend in the road as it drops back to Blaenavon, a green tip standing out from the heather marks where limestone was stockpiled to be collected by another tramroad below; the resultant sweetening of the acid soils has kept the heather at bay. Early scours and adits can be seen on both sides of the road.

The remains of a scour for washing away soil and exposing iron ore nodules, probably formed in about 1800. Keeper's Pond is in the distance, to the right (RCAHMW).

A small cast-iron boundary marker on the roadside above the western tunnel entrance at Pwll-du, with the letters BC° for 'Blaenavon Company' (Peter Wakelin).

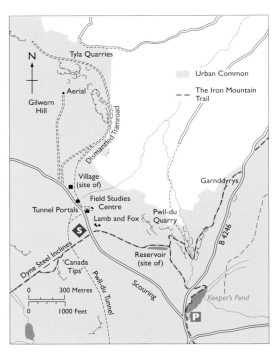

A Lost Quarry Village: Pwll-du

The minor road and footpaths opposite Keeper's Pond head north-west and follow the edge of the coal measures, where small tips and low dams for scouring can be made out. This tour begins opposite the Lamb and Fox. Start: **S**

The westernmost of the two northern portals of Pwll-du tramroad tunnel, driven through the mountain to Blaenavon by about 1815.

The Blaenavon company put housing wherever workers were needed, and Pwll-du was a community created in a spectacular but isolated position where the Pwll-du tramroad tunnel passed through the mountain. From around 1818 it was home to numerous families who worked in the adjacent mines and limestone quarries — there were sixty-three households here in 1851 — but the village was demolished in 1963. The open land is urban common offering interesting walks, but access to enclosed land is via rights of way only.

Pwll-du quarry lay to the east, but the largest of the quarries was Tyla, to the north, where quarry faces and waste tips are visible in the distance. The summit of Gilwern Hill behind the quarry was the limit of the Blaenavon company's landholding.

The first limestone tramroad to the ironworks passed the top edge of the fields and continued roughly along the line of the present road, then across the hilltop to Blaenavon [1].

This was a difficult summit to cross, and by about 1815 Pwll-du tunnel had been connected through the mountain (p. 61). The tunnel divided underground to emerge through two portals on this side of the mountain [2 & 3]. The two entrances lie about 110 yards (100m) along the road from the Lamb and Fox [4], near a dip with the turning to the Pwll-du field studies centre on the right. The low stone arches, passing underneath the road, took two wagons abreast, drawn by horses until steam haulage engines were installed in the late nineteenth century. The western portal [2] connected to the tramroad from Tyla quarries; the eastern portal [3] — currently largely hidden by soil overburden — to Pwll-du quarry and Garnddyrys forge, the slag heaps of which are visible on the slopes of the Blorenge. Branch tramroads went to nearby coal levels.

The community of Pwll-du was centred around Lower Rank [5], a row of thirty-one dwellings west of the tunnel portals, the curving platform of which can

be made out above the track. These were small houses, each with two rooms downstairs and a sleeping loft above reached by a ladder. Nearby there were a school, two chapels, two public houses, a company shop and another row of houses [6] built by 1829. The field studies centre was the Miners' Welfare Hall built on top of a coal tip [7] in the 1940s.

Returning to the road, opposite the Lamb and Fox, there is a track straight up the hill, signposted to Garn Lakes, which can be followed for a longer walk on the mountain. This was a standard-gauge railway incline [8] devised by the company engineer, Thomas Dyne Steel, in 1850. A pair of inclines brought coal over the mountain from Blaenavon to supply markets via Hill's tramroad and carried limestone back. Wagons on each side of the ridge counterbalanced one another, assisted by a steam winding engine. At the summit, the site of the engine house can be made out as a spread of rubble, with ponds nearby and the incline continuing down the opposite slope.

The track up from Pwll-du was concreted as a roadway for opencast mining begun as part of the war effort in 1943. Many pits producing steam coal had closed in the 1920s and 30s, so when coal was

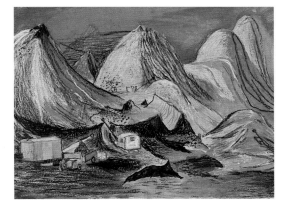

needed quickly during the Second World War the new methods were vital. The remains of the mines run along the ridge with more ancient workings visible at their edges: an extraordinary landscape, still black and unvegetated, that can be explored with caution. They were among the first strip mines in Britain, using North American expertise and dragline machines, and are still known as 'the Canada tips'. They are the only first-generation opencast mines to survive, and a unique reminder of wartime industry.

Above: An imaginative reconstruction of Pwll-du village as it might have appeared in the 1850s. Lower Rank, the curving row of thirty-one dwellings to the right, formed the centre of the community (Illustration by Michael Blackmore/Torfaen County Borough Council).

Left: The new opencast mines at Pwll-du, as depicted by Graham Sutherland (1903–80), who visited as an official war artist in 1943. These were among the first opencast mines in Britain, and remain little changed today (Estate of Graham Sutherland/ National Museum of Wales).

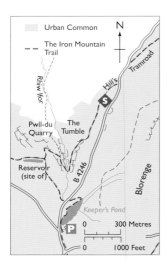

Right: Puddling furnaces and rolling mills at Cyfarthfa Ironworks, Merthyr Tydfil, painted by Penry Williams (1802–85) in 1825. A puddler can be seen working at a furnace on the right and rails are being drawn through rolls on the left (Cyfarthfa Castle Museum and Art Gallery, Merthyr Tydfil).

Puddling and Rolling: Garnddyrys Forge

The site of Garnddyrys forge is beside the B4246 from Blaenavon on the descent towards Abergavenny, just over one mile (1.6km) beyond Keeper's Pond. This tour begins at the footpath signposted to Pwll-du. Start: ◆ **S**

Garnddyrys is one of the most evocative places in the World Heritage Site. From 1817 to 1863 a bustling forge and its community stood on this mountainside, converting pig iron from Blaenavon Ironworks to wrought iron in puddling furnaces, and rolling bars and rails. In 1851 there were thirty-four households, two public houses and a school. From the roadside, you can see an oval depression ringed by a wall, which was once the reservoir that kept the waterwheels of Garnddyrys forge turning.

The terrace for the works is concealed beyond, but huge lumps of red brown slag are just visible to the left. Hill's tramroad (pp. 9–11) can be made out at the top of the valley as a shelf running from Pwll-du limestone quarry. Most of the site is urban common, allowing free access on foot, but fenced areas can be entered using rights of way only.

Forges converted pig iron into wrought iron and made bars and rails by rolling it in successive mills. Garnddyrys was built by the iron company as its main forge. At first it made bar iron with which to manufacture tinplate and cables, but in the 1840s it changed to making rails, then in high demand to build railways in Britain and across the world (p. 13). However, the location of the works made sense only while the company used Hill's tramroad as their export route. After the standard-gauge railway arrived in Blaenavon, the Forgeside plant was put into production and Garnddyrys was dismantled.

From the road, follow the graded track signposted to Pwll-du. The path leads downhill, past the former reservoir on your right [1], and curves around to the right, past the site of the manager's house [2], to the platform of the works. A retaining wall was cut into

Above: One of the huge lumps of slag that lie to the south-west of the Garnddyrys forge site.

Opposite: An aerial photograph of Garnddyrys forge site from the south (RCAHMW).

The process of wrought-iron making was depicted in 1874 by T. H. Thomas (1834–1915) in the forge of Treforest tinplate works. In forges like Garnddyrys, cast iron was remelted in reverberatory furnaces. Here, it was stirred by a puddler (right) until a ball of iron weighing perhaps 110lb (50kg) could be lifted out. The work of the puddler was notoriously skilled and arduous. The ball of iron from the puddling furnace was 'shingled', or beaten (far right), to drive off impurities, under a steam-powered or water-powered hammer (National Museum of Wales).

The resulting 'blooms' of hammered iron were rolled, reheated and rolled again into bars or rails, as shown in this photograph of the Tredegar Ironworks rolling mills in 1912 (National Museum of Wales).

Below: The remains of the balance shaft (visible at top left) at Pwll-du quarry, probably built by James Ashwell around 1839, when the ironworks balance tower was constructed.

the slope, as at Blaenavon Ironworks, but it is much eroded [3]. High up, near the centre of the wall, is the sluice through which water reached a large waterwheel. There would have been constant noise and labour here: the terrace contained multiple puddling furnaces, hammers and rolling mills [4], powered in the 1830s by two steam engines. Slag was dumped down the slope beyond [5]. A tunnel, almost 600 feet (180m) long, carried through-traffic on Hill's tramroad under the tips [6]; the works itself was served by branch lines in both directions [7]. Just beyond the far end of the terrace are rubble piles, which are all that remains of a three-sided court of workers' houses, similar to Stack Square (pp. 23–25) [8]. A further row of ten houses stood across the road.

Spectacular walks can be taken in both directions from Garnddyrys along Hill's tramroad, now the Iron Mountain Trail. The route to the north continues on the opposite side of the B4246. This gives panoramic views of the Usk valley for a mile (1.6km) or so, before reaching another small tunnel and the head of the inclines that lowered traffic to the canal (p. 59). From this point, adventurous walkers can continue up the Blorenge or down to the wharf at Llanfoist.

The route south from Garnddyrys returns through the works and past another former reservoir [9] on an elevated, level course to Pwll-du quarry. The tramroad doglegs into the Tumble, supported by stone walls, passes the remains of a small stone cabin and is crossed by the ancient road, 'Rhiw Ifor', cut through the rock as it climbs from Cwm Llanwenarth to Blaenavon. A branch tramroad once dropped from here to the quarry floor. But continuing on the level, before you reach a fence, it is possible to look down into the quarry where the fragmentary masonry remains of a balance shaft are visible. The balance lifted limestone 130 feet (40m) to the tramroad, its lower part cut through the solid rock. The water came from an earth-banked tank above the tramroad and a higher reservoir. Do not cross the stile as the shaft is open and unfenced, but walk back a little way and up to the former reservoir (see p. 64 and photograph p.46) where there is an excellent view of Garnddyrys and the quarry as well as Abergavenny and the Usk valley. From 1818 to the late 1850s, Pwll-du quarry supplied kilns in Llanfoist, from where burnt lime was traded on the Llanvihangel tramroad as far as Abergavenny and Hereford.

Canal Transport: Govilon Wharf and Llanfoist

Govilon wharf is beside the B4246 from Blaenavon to Abergavenny. Passing downhill, after two hairpin bends cross over the canal bridge. After 65 yards (60m) turn left to British Waterways' Govilon Wharf, and then immediately left into the car park. A level return walk of 2.5 miles (4km) to Llanfoist wharf takes 60–90 minutes. Alternative parking is available in Llanfoist village.

Canals were the prime arteries of the Industrial Revolution, and the Brecknock & Abergavenny Canal carried Blaenavon's iron, coal and lime as well as incoming supplies. The Brecknock & Abergavenny was connected to the Monmouthshire Canal at Pontymoile and thence to the sea at Newport in 1812. Some of the earliest railway warehouses in the world survive at Govilon and Llanfoist wharves. Hill's tramroad descended to Llanfoist by a chain of dramatic inclined planes completed in 1818. The Blaenavon company was now able to take advantage of the new canal's favourable tolls.

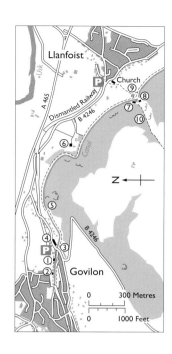

Leave the car park via the entrance and turn left. Further along, enter the gateway on the right onto the old railway line. Opposite this is a white building with a hipped roof (Govilon Boat Club) [1]. This is believed to have been a warehouse for Blaenavon Ironworks, built when Thomas Hill II leased a wharf near the road around 1814–16. The tiny scale of the building seems odd today, but pig iron would have been stacked on the quay, and only more delicate cast objects or imported goods would be kept inside. Hill's tramroad crosses the slope of the Blorenge behind the treeline, working its way around from Garnddyrys to the inclines at Llanfoist.

Work on the canal began in 1793 under the engineer, John Dadford, and his brother, Thomas, but owing to financial difficulties it took nineteen years to complete. For seven years, from 1805, the canal stopped here, an isolated waterway to Brecon. In common with other south Wales canals it carried double-ended boats, 60 feet (18m) long by 8 feet (2.5m) wide, with canvas awnings instead of cabins — quite unlike the narrow boats of the English canal network. Each boat could carry 25 tons and was pulled by a single horse.

A further 55 yards (50m) along the railway line you can look down on Crawshay Bailey's warehouse [2], now offices for British Waterways. The warehouse was built in 1821 for iron brought from Nantyglo Ironworks, transhipped here from

A photograph showing a characteristic boat of the south Wales canals. These had prows at both ends to obviate the need to turn them, and were towed by one horse from the tall post visible in the photograph (John Lewis).

Opposite: At Govilon wharf stands Bailey's warehouse, built in 1821 for iron brought by tramroad from Nantyglo. The white building may have been a warehouse for iron brought by turnpike road from Blaenavon, before Hill's tramroad to Llanfoist was completed.

Left: The warehouse at Llanfoist wharf built by Thomas Hill II after his tramroad connected Blaenavon to the Brecknock & Abergavenny Canal in 1818. The incline passed up the hillside from between the warehouse and the wharf keeper's house.

Bailey's tramroad. The bracket for a crane can be seen at the corner of the building.

Walk across the old railway bridge over the canal and down the footpath on your left. Turn right on the canal towpath, passing the warehouses on the other side of the canal. The typical canal bridge [3] has a horseshoe-shaped arch and room for the towpath to pass underneath. The three-storey house beyond the bridge [4] has its own wharf and a Georgian doorcase facing the canal rather than the road. This was once a coal transhipment yard between the canal and the Llanvihangel tramroad, which opened to Abergavenny in 1814.

From here the canal snakes along the contours, cut into the hill on one side and built out on the other. Bridge 96 is a 'turnover' bridge, where the towpath changes sides [5]: it was designed to allow the horse to cross without detaching the tow rope (by going over and under the bridge). Beyond this, some small sandstone quarries can be made out amid the trees.

The canal narrows in several places over the next mile (1.6km). Stop-gates at these points could close off the water supply in the event of a breach in the high embankment. Just beyond the first stop-gate position, the canal crosses a hillside gully. The Georgian mansion, Llanfoist House, is below [6]. Built in the late eighteenth century, it was the home of the Blaenavon Ironworks partner, Robert Wheeley, in the 1840s, and later of Crawshay Bailey of Nantyglo, one of the most famous ironmasters in Wales.

The next section passed through hard rock, so the canal was made narrower to save expense. Arriving at

Llanfoist wharf, the long warehouse [7], with a hipped slate roof, was built for Hill's tramroad — a branch line ran inside, behind the pillars. The tramroad continued over the bridge [8], which is built of four iron beams with a deck of iron plates, and down to Llanfoist village, where the company owned a bank of limekilns. Traffic could continue as far as Hereford via the Llanvihangel tramroad.

If you take the steps down the embankment [9] opposite the warehouse (noting one step carved 'B&A Co' for the canal company), you can pass through a tunnel that once carried the parish road under both the canal and the wharf keeper's house. The path beyond this leads to the bottom of the inclines plunging down through the woods [10]. Stone sleeper blocks can be found in places and two replica trams stand at the bottom of the inclines. Carrying long bars of iron down the inclines could be particularly difficult, and according to the company engineer 'wild runs' were frequent. It is possible to climb the inclines to the level line of Hill's tramroad back to Garnddyrys, or even to the summit of the Blorenge.

You can return to Govilon on the towpath, or by taking the steep lane down the hill. In the graveyard of the medieval church of Llanfoist, at the bottom of the lane, are an obelisk to Crawshay Bailey and the tomb of Robert Wheeley. Across the main road from the church, you can follow the disused railway out of the far end of the small car park directly to Govilon wharf.

Three inclines (above) brought iron, coal and limestone to Llanfoist wharf. Many stone sleeper blocks can still be seen. A replica section of plateway and wagons have been erected at the wharf (below) (Torfaen County Borough Council).

Tramroads to the Furnaces: The Upper Yard, Pwll-du Tunnel and the Lost Viaduct

Go up the hill at the front of the ironworks on North Street, then turn left towards Brynmawr, along the B4248. About 450 yards (400m) from the junction, there is an entrance on the right into a large turning area. The open land is urban common, but enclosed areas can only be entered using rights of way. There are designated car parks at the ironworks and Riflegreen. Start: **S**

Below right: Sir Richard Colt Hoare's drawing of the Blaenavon viaduct in about 1798. His travelling companion William Coxe described it has having ten arches. The bridge appears to have had a roof put across the deck to keep the two-storey cottages beneath the arches dry. Within a few years the valley had completely filled with spoil; and the bridge is not shown on any surviving map (© Yale Centre for British Art, Paul Mellon Collection, USA/Bridgeman Art Library).

Below: The excavation by television's Time Team for the viaduct in 2000 found a tunnel on the supposed line of the bridge, 33 feet (10m) below the current surface. This picture shows the extraordinary depth of spoil filling the original valley of Cwm Dwfn, thought to be 82 feet (25m) at its deepest (Peter Wakelin).

The area below the road is immediately behind the ironworks. It was the hub of the company's tramroad system and the yard where raw materials were delivered. Standing here two centuries ago you would be shrouded in fumes from smouldering coke heaps. There were also limekilns, a smithy, and workers' cottages. In March 2000, excavations were conducted in search of the earliest railway viaduct in the world, which is known to have crossed a deep valley that was later buried by spoil from the mines. The vestiges of the valley are to the north, where the Pwll-du tramroad tunnel entered the mountain, but at this point its floor was some 82 feet (25m) below the present surface. The surrounding hillside is scarred by workings for coal and iron ore dating from the seventeenth century and later.

The viaduct was built to carry coal and ore wagons across Cwm Dwfn (or 'deep valley') when the ironworks was set out around 1788. When Coxe and Colt Hoare saw it in 1798 there were two-storey miners' cottages beneath the arches. But within a few more years, the whole structure had been buried, along with the valley itself. The tramroad was kept operational only by building a tunnel over it. It is hard to imagine the vast quantities of material moved as the hills were literally turned inside out. Scouring (indicated by the place name Race Sych or 'Dry Scour') would have washed down waste material, but mine spoil was also dumped here. The stream in the valley bottom remained the parish boundary for

decades after it was culverted and buried. Turning to look towards the hill, one hedged field on the left suggests the line of the contours before mining began. Fan-shaped tips from coal and iron ore levels, which perforated the hillside, survive all around; the wartime opencast mines dominate the horizon.

A short walk, following the valley, leads to the ruins of some cottages and stables, and the fragmentary southern entrance to Pwll-du tunnel

(p. 52). The tunnel appears to have been begun as a mining level on this site in the 1780s, but it was extended through the mountain to Pwll-du in about 1815. At almost a mile and a half (2.4km), it was the longest tramroad tunnel then built, and remained the longest on any horse-drawn route. It carried most of the limestone to Blaenavon and, as part of Hill's tramroad, was the main export route for the ironworks from 1818 until the 1860s.

The remains of Cwm Dwfn, the valley that was largely infilled by mining spoil that was produced from 1788 onwards. The southern entrance to Pwll-du tunnel was at the end of the valley. Old workings rise up the hill to the opencast workings at the summit.

Alexander Cordell

Alexander Cordell was the pen name of the historical novelist George Alexander Graber (1914–97), whose most famous book, *The Rape of the Fair Country*, was set in and around Blaenavon in the 1820s and 1830s. Inspired by his meetings with Blaenavon people when he lived nearby at Llanellen, and underpinned by subsequent historical research, it told a powerful story of a family coming to find dangerous work in the mines and ironworks, against a backdrop of strife in a new community and the transformation of Monmouthshire's green hillsides. Following its

publication in 1959, it became a bestseller and was translated into seventeen languages. The *New York Times* praised it as one of the most memorable novels of the year. Cordell wrote thirty books in all, including two sequels tracing the Industrial Revolution in south Wales, *The Hosts of Rebecca* and *The Song of the Earth. This Proud and Savage Land* was also set in Blaenavon. The Welsh historian Gwyn A. Williams regarded him as a 'giant figure' who, by investigating the lives of working people, had 'succeeded where historians failed'. Cordell maintained a strong interest in Blaenavon and the ironworks. A display of material at Blaenavon Community Heritage and Cordell Museum, adjacent to Blaenavon Library, includes his writing desk.

Alexander Cordell at Blaenavon Ironworks in the 1990s (Western Mail and Echo Ltd).

Colliery and Steelworks: Big Pit and Forgeside

From the ironworks car park, turn left through the industrial estate to Big Pit: National Coal Museum, on the opposite side of the valley. For Big Pit's opening hours, telephone 01495 790311.

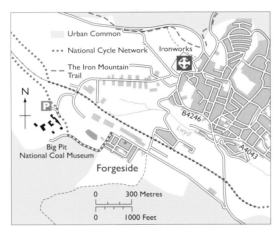

Below: The cluster of buildings around the headframe at Big Pit, looking across the valley to Blaenavon. The winding house is to the right and the smiths' shop in the foreground. The furnaces at Forgeside stood just downhill, and the forge and steel plant to the right (Peter Wakelin).

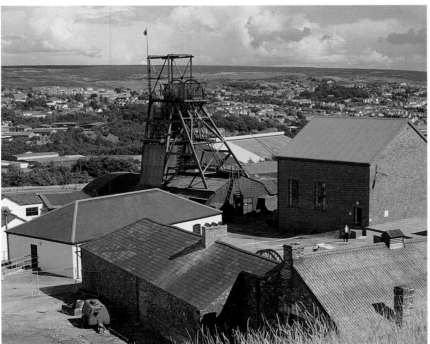

In the late 1830s the new Blaenavon Iron Company chose their freehold land in this part of the valley for a major development. Work began on the construction of new blast furnaces, a forge and pits. But progress was halted and it was not until 1859 that the forge finally went into production and Forgeside village was built. Blast furnaces were erected from 1868, and a steel-making plant was commissioned in 1877 (pp. 12–14). Big Pit opened in 1880, becoming the principal colliery in the area for a century. Consisting of an irregular group of structures of varying dates, its development was typical of many south Wales mines.

Big Pit's buildings cluster around the shaft top, above a high wall for loading rail wagons. The entrance is through the former fitting shop of 1911, the electrical workshops and the managers' offices. These lead to the pithead with its towering steel headframe built in 1921: the squealing of winding gears was a familiar sound throughout south Wales, but only a handful now survive. Coal drams coming up the shaft were emptied onto sorting screens on the downhill side, and shunted around the circuit under a ramshackle corrugated-iron roof, ready to return down the shaft. New investment was made at Big Pit following the nationalization of the coal industry in 1947 and included the construction of the present winding-engine house with its electric winder in 1952. The smiths' shops and the sawmill for preparing pit props are also on this level.

Visitors to the underground workings travel in the cages to the pit bottom. The shaft is of the oval form typical of water-balance pits, and was sunk in the abortive development of the 1830s before being put into commission around 1880. The tour includes typical roadways and sections of coalface, a haulage engine, the ventilation doorways once worked by children, and stables for pit ponies. Some of the workings date from before 1830, when these seams were exploited from Forge Level, rising from the riverbank.

Returning to the surface, the steps lead to the most architecturally distinguished building on the site, the baths of 1939, constructed in the International style. Baths like this were built throughout Britain after the Miners' Welfare Committee was established in 1921 to raise levies on coal production, which were used to build baths run by independent trustees. Over 400 pithead baths were completed during the next thirty years — fifty-two of them in 1939 alone. They revolutionized the lives of miners by providing canteens, laundries and medical rooms, and by saving them from walking home across the mountain covered in coal dust and wet-through, as generations had done before them. For women at home, they removed the backbreaking work of preparing tin baths and doing daily washing. Miners passed through the showers from the 'dirty' side to the 'clean' side, with their own heated lockers in each. Big Pit's baths provided for 792 men.

Other buildings on this level include the headgear from a typical south Wales water-balance shaft, brought here from Tredegar, a fan house for ventilating the underground workings and an explosives store.

The terrace outside the baths is an excellent viewpoint. The whitewashed cottages of Stack Square mark out the ironworks, with the town to its right. The intense exploitation of the mountain is clear, with its complex pattern of tips and scours and the wartime opencast mines at the summit. The river was culverted in the nineteenth century and the valley was filled with slag where the industrial estate now stands. The forge, steelworks and coke ovens covered the slope below Big Pit, but only the far end of the site remains: the red brick former power house and Doncaster's modern forge, continuing the long tradition of metalworking in Blaenavon. The village of Forgeside is beyond. Its first streets were named by the dour ironmasters simply Row A, B, C, D and E.

The pithead baths at Big Pit, designed by A. J. Saise in 1939. The architects of the Miners' Welfare Committee were influenced by Modernist architecture in Holland, expressing the functional spaces within the building in the external shapes. The buildings were innovative in using double-skinned walls for insulation, flat roofs and reinforced concrete (National Museum of Wales).

Further Reading

Acknowledgements

The author and Cadw would like to thank Michael Blackmore, John Cornwell, Jane Cresswell, Professor John Elliott, John Evans, Clive Gardiner, John Hilling, Francis Keen, Richard Keen, Jeremy Knight, Martin Lawler, John Lewis, Dr M. J. T. Lewis, Jeremy Lowe, Gareth Phillips, Robert Protheroe Jones, John Rodger, Ian Standing, Professor Jennifer Tann, Harry Thornton, Dr Barrie Trinder, Dr John van Laun, and staff of Cadw, the West Glamorgan and Gwent record offices, and the Royal Commission on the Ancient and Historical Monuments of Wales.

www.world-heritage-blaenavon.org.uk   www.cadw.wales.gov.uk
www.rcahmw.org.uk   www.cordellcountry.org

Association for Industrial Archaeology, *A Powerhouse of Industry: A Guide to Industrial Archaeological Sites in South-East Wales* (Cardiff 2003).

Michael Atkinson and Colin Baber, *The Growth and Decline of the South Wales Iron Industry 1760–1880: An Industrial History*, University of Wales Board of Celtic Studies Social Science Monographs 9 (Cardiff 1987).

Chris Barber, *Exploring Blaenavon Industrial Landscape World Heritage Site* (Abergavenny 2002).

Lewis Browning, *Blaenavon, Monmouthshire: A Brief Historical Sketch* (Abergavenny 1906; reprinted Cowbridge 1988).

Neil Cossons, *The BP Book of Industrial Archaeology*, second edition (Newton Abbott 1993).

J. A. H. Evans, 'The Evolution of Blaenavon Town', *Gwent Local History* **94** (Spring 2003), 34–54.

Chris Evans, *Labyrinth of Flames: Work and Social Conflict in Early Merthyr* (Cardiff 1993).

W. K. V. Gale, *The British Iron and Steel Industry* (Cardiff 1967).

Stephen Hughes, Brian Malaws, Medwyn Parry and Peter Wakelin, *Collieries of Wales: Engineering and Architecture* (Aberystwyth 1995).

Laurence Ince, *The South Wales Iron Industry 1750–1885* (Birmingham 1993).

A. H. John, *The Industrial Development of South Wales 1750–1850* (Cardiff 1950; second edition 1995).

Jeremy K. Knight, *Blaenavon Ironworks* (Cardiff 1989; revised second edition 1992).

Jeremy K. Knight, 'Brought Forth in a High Place: Religion, Society and Language in 19th Century Blaenavon', *Monmouthshire Antiquary* **16** (2000), 121–130.

John Lewis and Malcolm Thomas, *Blaenavon through the Years in Photographs*, volumes I–III (Abertillery 1987, 1988, 1993).

Jeremy Lowe, *Welsh Industrial Workers' Housing 1775–1875* (Cardiff 1977).

J. B. Lowe, 'Housing as a Source for Industrial History: A Case Study of Blaenavon', *IA: Journal of the Society for Industrial Archeology* **8 (1)** (1982), 13–36.

J. Lowe and M. Lawler, 'Landscapes of the Iron Industry at Blaenafon, Gwent', *Landscape History* **2** (1980), 71–82.

Gordon Rattenbury, *Tramroads of the Brecknock & Abergavenny Canal* (Oakham 1980).

D. Morgan Rees, *The Industrial Archaeology of Wales* (Newton Abbot 1975).

Philip Riden and John G. Owen, *British Blast Furnace Statistics 1790–1980* (Cardiff 1995).

Barrie Trinder, *The Making of the Industrial Landscape*, second edition (London 1997).

John van Laun, *Early Limestone Railways: How Railways Developed to Feed the Furnaces of the Industrial Revolution in South East Wales* (London 2001).

Peter Wakelin, 'Scouring the Land: Early Iron Ore Extraction at Blaenavon', *Monmouthshire Antiquary* **12** (1996), 62–67.

Forge Level, which connects to Big Pit and probably dates from the 1830s (The National Monuments Record of Wales: John Cornwell Collection).

A Tour of the Landscape

Other Features of Interest

9 **Bailey's Bridge** — A bridge of 1821 built for Bailey's tramroad from Nantyglo Ironworks to the canal at Govilon. D1

10 **Llanwenarth Baptist Church, Govilon** — A chapel begun in 1695, with surviving eighteenth-century gallery and box pews. D1

11 **Govilon Aqueduct** — This carried the Brecknock & Abergavenny Canal over a road. The canal opened from Brecon in 1805, but was not completed eastwards until 1812. D1

12 **Llanfoist Inclines** — Four counterbalanced inclines, which dropped Hill's tramroad 300 yards (280m) down the Blorenge; they were finished in 1818. The first three went to Llanfoist wharf and the fourth continued to limekilns and a junction with the Llanvihangel tramroad. F2

13 **St Faith's Church, Llanfoist** — The church may have thirteenth-century origins, but it was largely rebuilt in 1872. In the churchyard are monuments to the ironmasters, Crawshay Bailey and Robert Wheeley, and the Blaenavon company doctors, the Steeles. F1

14 **Blorenge Quarry Road** — A cart road or possibly a plateway built from limestone quarries to the ironworks around 1795. It fell into disuse in 1804, but the route is undisturbed. E2

15 **Blorenge Tunnel** — Built in 1818, the tunnel allowed Hill's tramroad to continue its level route without leaving the common. Excellent runs of stone sleeper blocks survive nearby. E2

16 **Craig-yr-hafod Limekiln** — An agricultural limekiln with adjacent quarries, which was in use in 1811. A track connects it to a coal level up the hill. E4

17 **Tyla Limestone Railroad** — The route to take lime to the ironworks followed the present road then curved across the fields. It may possibly have been the first line anywhere to use all-iron rails, about 1789. If so, it was converted to a plateway around 1800 and a standard-gauge railway in 1885. C2

18 **Tyla Quarries** — The most important source of limestone for the ironworks from about 1789 until the 1940s; from 1885 with Gilwern Hill quarry. C2

19 **Pwll-du Quarry** — Limestone from this quarry, owned by Walter Lewis, was taken to kilns at Llanfoist, and perhaps to the ironworks. By 1819 it was served by a branch from Hill's tramroad, but as the quarry extended deeper a water-balance lift was built, probably in the 1830s (its reservoir is on the hill above). C3

20 **Scouring at Pwll-du** — Broken ground caused by scouring for iron ore survives in a strip parallel with the road. C3

21 **Dyne Steel Inclines** — A railway built in 1850 to bring limestone from Tyla quarries, the Dyne Steel inclines supplemented Pwll-du tunnel. The inclines are clear on both slopes of the ridge, and the positions of the steam winding engine, pond, and engine man's cottage can be detected at the summit. B3

22 **Wartime Opencasts** — Started in 1943 and known as the 'Canada tips', after the Canadian troops who introduced steam shovel technology here, this was the first strip mine in Britain. It was recorded by the war artist Graham Sutherland. (p. 53) C3

23 **Hill Pits** — A colliery that was worked between 1844 and 1893. Tips, enclosures and building foundations surround a chimney for the winding engine. B4

24 **Hill Pits Incline** — The level line of a tramroad from Hill Pits leads to an incline down to the ironworks, built around 1840. At the top, the brake for the counterbalance wheel survives in a stone-lined pit. C4

25 **Garn Road Powder Store** — A nineteenth-century powder store with a curtain wall and brick vault, which helped to contain explosions. C4

26 **Pwll-du Tunnel** — Begun as a mine before 1800, by 1815 the tunnel cut through the mountain: at 1.5 miles (2.4km) it was the longest ever built on a horse-drawn railway. The line was extended to Llanfoist in 1818. (For portals see pp. 52, 61) C3

27 **Upper Brickyard** — This was one of three yards making firebricks for the ironworks. It was probably built in 1788 and still in use in the 1920s. The sheds and kilns have gone, but clay pits, tips and tramroads can be traced near walls made of waste bricks and tuyères. C4

28 **St James's Church** — The church was built between 1911 and 1914 using stone from the old furnaces. C4

29 **Engine Pit** — A coal mine sunk around 1806. An underground waterwheel pumped water from lower workings. At the surface is the base of a later steam engine. Another is believed to survive below ground. C5

30 **River Arch** — The entrance to the culvert built to carry the Afon Lwyd beneath slag heaps in the mid-nineteenth century. The culvert joins Forge Level, which connects to Big Pit. (p. 63) C5

31 **Iron Bridge** — A bridge built between 1812 and 1818 by Aaron Brute to carry trams to a coal level. C5

32 **Company Farm** — A farm on land purchased by the ironworks in 1810 and managed by William Allgood. C5

33 **Forgeside** — A settlement established in the 1860s by the Blaenavon Iron Company alongside its new forge (pp. 13, 63). The rows were named A, B, C, D and E. Zion Baptist Church on Forge Road was built around 1874–76. West of the village is a brick power house to generate electricity for the steelworks, and below it, the steelworks site and forge manager's house. C5

34 **Coity Quarry and Incline** — Opened before 1844, it supplied sandstone to build houses and the Forgeside works. The winding drum for the incline remains. B5

35 **Pontypool and Blaenavon Railway** — This section of the London and North Western Railway was completed in 1869. It is open to visitors with a variety of steam and diesel rolling stock. B4

36 **Capel Newydd** — The site of a late medieval chapel serving the sparse population before the growth of Blaenavon; it fell out of use in the 1860s and was demolished around 1893. E6

37 **Forge Row, Cwmavon** — Twelve cottages of about 1804 built for the forge, which was in the valley below. The stone roofs and chimneys and whitewashed frontage show the character of early workers' houses and contrast with the adjacent manager's home, Cwmavon House. E7

38 **Westlake's Brewery** — Now a factory, this multi-storey brewery was built in 1900. Brewing stopped in 1928. E7

39 **Varteg** — The site of an ironworks established on a sub-lease from Blaenavon partners in 1803 and operating until 1864. Workers' houses, a former pond and an incline to the valley remain. D7